MW00649196

Editor: Jennifer Miller

Authors: Amy Copeland, Keith Dudhnath, Barry Edwards, Keith Gillespie, Jon Gorman, Daniel Graham, Mark Hogan, Chris Jonason, Paul Jones, Matt McLay, Julie Munger, Chris Onions, Paul O'Sullivan, Abigail Polsby, Julie Munger, Geraint Rowlands, Jim Segerstrom, J Michael Turnbull and Phil Turnbull

Illustrations: Carol Davies, George Manley, Rick Webber

Photos: Chris Cieszko, Julie Munger, Devon and Somerset Fire and Rescue Service, Keith Dudhnath, Rescue 3 Greece, Raven Rescue, Dan Wheeley, J Michael Turnbull, or as credited

Layout: Vicky Barlow & Jennifer Miller

Version: 6.1

Safety notice

This Rescue 3 International manual is a basic text to be used in conjunction with Rescue 3 classes taught by instructors certified by Rescue 3 International. Utilization of this material without certified instruction may be hazardous to life and limb.

Scope of manual

This manual is designed as an accompanying reference for those undertaking Rescue 3 training. It is not a standalone document and does not replace training by a qualified instructor.

These notes are designed to provide initial pre-course reading, and to act as a post-training resource.

Training courses are only one part in the development of competent rescuers. Without post-training practice and experience, students will be unable to develop the necessary levels of skill and judgment to allow them to operate effectively as rescuers in a swiftwater and flood environment.

Contents

Section 7: Incident management

Section 8: Specialist rescues

Appendices

About Rescue 3 International

Rescue 3 International produces and delivers state of the art technical rescue training courses.

More than 500,000 students have taken Rescue 3's water, rope, boat and confined space courses. Since 1979 Rescue 3 has delivered its training in over 62 countries to fire and rescue services, ambulance teams, mountain rescue teams, industrial and resource personnel, and commercial training and leisure activity providers.

The flagship Rescue 3 courses are Swiftwater and Flood Rescue Technician (SRT), Technical Rope Rescue Technician (TRR), Swiftwater and Flood Rescue Boat Operator (SFRBO) and Confined Space Rescue Technician (CSRT). Rescue 3 also has supporting courses, offering awareness qualifications, through to advanced technician and management-level qualifications.

There are over 1500 Rescue 3 certified instructors throughout the world, delivering courses for a wide array of Rescue 3 training providers in many different industries. These are within the fire and rescue services, industrial companies, mountain rescue and water rescue teams, and other outdoor professional establishments. Additionally, there are a number of training centers who offer Rescue 3 courses on a commercial basis.

The reputation for quality hands-on instruction, using techniques that work, has fueled the growth of Rescue 3 and its courses.

History

Rescue 3 International was started in 1979 by a group of people involved with emergency services, who identified a need for training in areas not commonly covered in the emergency training programs of the time.

The name, Rescue 3, was chosen when the company first started, because the instruction was concerned with all areas of rescue - land, air, and water - thus Rescue 3.

In 1981, the program was redesigned into an early form of the current Swiftwater Rescue Technician curriculum. Swiftwater classes were taught throughout California and slowly spread across the United States.

In late 1990, Rescue 3 became Rescue 3 International Incorporated. Over the course of the next several years, Rescue 3 International went on to develop instructor teams throughout the United States and around the globe.

In 1999, there was a major revision in the curriculum to meet the requirements of the new NFPA[1] 1670 and 1006 standards. The years since have been a period of great growth of internationally accredited technical rescue training. Rescue 3 has developed a number of specialized Rescue 3 courses in a variety of markets to meet the ever-increasing demand for internationally recognized rescue training of the highest standards.

---

1   National Fire Protection Association

Progressing within Rescue 3

Student qualifications

Rescue 3 International offers courses in a variety of technical rescue specialties, including water, rope, boat and confined space. These are delivered at all levels, including awareness, operations, technician, advanced technician, and management.

Instructor qualifications

There are Rescue 3 International instructor qualifications for every level of student course. These can be for both commercial course delivery, or for delivery within an agency (e.g., a fire and rescue service).

Training providers

Instructors delivering Rescue 3 courses must do so for a Rescue 3 training provider. Training providers can either be commercial, or agency (i.e., delivering in-house).

There is a simple yet robust application process for becoming a Rescue 3 training provider. For training provider criteria and application forms, or to discuss the options available, please contact the Rescue 3 International office.

Accreditation checks

To check the status or validity of a Rescue 3 training provider, instructor or student, please contact the Rescue 3 International office.

Upon request, Rescue 3 International can also provide an organization with due dates for recertification for their Rescue 3 qualified staff.

All Rescue 3 student qualifications are valid for a period of 3 years from the end date of the course. To maintain continuous certification, recertification must take place before the end of these 3 years.

Recertification can be at the same level as the initial course. Alternatively, you can add an additional skill-set by taking a higher level course. For example, you could recertify a Swiftwater and Flood Rescue Technician (SRT) course, by taking either a Rescues from Vehicles in Water (RVW) or Swiftwater and Flood Rescue Technician Advanced (SRTA) course.

Rescue 3 contact details

For a list of course providers in your area, please contact Rescue 3.

Rescue 3 International

11084 Jeff Brian Lane
PO Box 1050
Wilton
California 95693
USA

Telephone   916 687 6556
Toll Free   800 457 3728

Website   www.rescue3.com
Email   info@rescue3.com

Rescue 3 Europe Ltd

The Malthouse
Regent Street
Llangollen
Denbighshire
LL20 8HS
UK

Telephone   +44 (0) 1978 869 069

Website   www.rescue3europe.com
Email   info@rescue3europe.com

Rescue 3 Canada / Raven Rescue

Box 861
Smithers BC V0J 2N0
Canada

Telephone   250 847 2427
Toll Free   800 880 0287

Website   www.ravenrescue.com
Email   info@ravenrescue.com

1   RESCUE PRINCIPLES AND PHILOSOPHY

Flooding in North Carolina during Tropical Storm Nicole (2010)

Photo: Chris Cieszko

1

SECTION CONTENTS

Rescue 3 philosophy

1

Rescue 3 considers there to be four elements which combine to create a successful rescue:

- Training
- Practice
- Experience
- Judgment

For a team to be successful in their actions, they must first undertake a course of instruction to gain foundation training. In order to become more proficient, they should practice these skills and techniques further, therefore gaining experience. This may include practice at particular sites that have historically proved problematic, and can be integrated into the pre-plan for the site or area.

As the team becomes more experienced and practiced, they will develop good, sound judgment when dealing with the variety of situations. This judgment is vital when the teams are faced with rescue situations in challenging conditions. It is their judgment that will be relied upon to make the right decisions on how (or how not) to proceed with a rescue.

Having gained experience of what works, what has problems, what are the advantages and disadvantages for various systems, and what the solutions are, the team will have the judgment to be able to choose the best solution for any situation without wasting time. This judgment cannot be purchased, or fast-tracked; it is the result of time spent practicing and gaining experience in a variety of conditions and applications.

Rescue priorities

At all incidents, the priorities of all rescuers should be:

- Self
- Team
- Victim

It is vitally important to take responsibility for your own actions. This includes your safety in a hazardous environment such as a rescue site. Unless correctly trained and equipped, the task could be unachievable and produce more casualties. Acting on uneducated and misjudged impulses, such as jumping in the water unequipped or untrained to save a person, is highly likely to result in tragedy rather than success. It is paramount that rescuers do not operate beyond their capability.

The statement above also extends to the team. Individuals have a responsibility to look after their team members and not place them in danger to a level beyond control. It is necessary to have backup systems in place so that team members' safety is protected, ensuring operations follow safe systems of work. It is essential that all the team look after their own safety by avoiding undue risks.

Only when the rescuer has provided for their own safety, and their team's safety, can they start to perform rescues or operate in a water environment. Any work or rescue cannot exceed the team's capability.

Finally, after ensuring the safety of themselves, the team and the victim, the risks taken for the retrieval of equipment should be very low – the equipment is replaceable, but people are not!

The best rescue is one that does not need to be performed.

Water rescue training standards

1

Rescue 3 standards

This course is delivered to the internationally-recognized Rescue 3 standards. These set out the course requirements, best practice, relevant knowledge and techniques required for an individual trained to this level. This alignment of skills ensures that a rescuer trained to a defined level in Maryland is at the same level of an equivalent rescuer in California, Ontario, or the UK.

For multi-agency, multi-jurisdictional, multi-regional and even multi-national operations, this consistency of knowledge and skills ensures vital interoperability, leading to safer and more effective rescues.

NFPA 1670 and 1006 standards

The National Fire Protection Association (NFPA) is an American organization that develops and publishes standards on both equipment and operations. Unlike most European Standards, they are not mandatory. An organization can decide if it wishes to be compliant with the standard. In NFPA terminology, the organization which wishes to meet the standard is referred to as the Authority Having Jurisdiction or AHJ. The NFPA does not audit against the standards. It is the responsibility of the AHJ to show that they have met the requirements of the published standard.

In 1998, the NFPA published NFPA 1670 – a rescue standard that addresses water rescue as one of its components. In 2000, NFPA 1006 was released, which sets minimum standards for emergency response personnel who perform technical rescue operations, including water and flood rescues.

While the NFPA might be seen as American-focused, application of the standards is not limited to the USA. Currently, they are the only existing standards that relate to water and flood rescue operations and so are used across Canada as well as in many other countries.

NFPA 1670 – Standard on operations and training for technical search and rescue incidents (revised 2017)

The intent of this standard is to establish general guidelines for an organization (AHJ) in assessing hazards, identifying levels of operational capabilities and establishing training documentation and response guidelines. The standard addresses the following rescue disciplines:

- Rope Rescue
- Structural Collapse Search and Rescue
- Confined Space Search and Rescue
- Vehicle Search and Rescue
- Animal Technical Rescue
- Wilderness Search and Rescue
- Trench Search and Rescue
- Machinery Search and Rescue
- Cave Search and Rescue
- Mine and Tunnel Search and Rescue

- Helicopter Search and Rescue
- Surface Water Search and Rescue
- Swiftwater Search and Rescue
- Dive Search and Rescue
- Ice Search and Rescue
- Surf Search and Rescue
- Watercraft Search and Rescue
- Flood Search and Rescue
- Tower Search and Rescue

1

Levels of Functional Capability

NFPA 1670 identifies three levels of functional capability for technical rescue. It is the responsibility of the AHJ to decide which level or levels it wishes to safely and effectively conduct operations at technical rescue incidents. The three levels are:

Awareness   Minimum capabilities of any responder who, in the course of their regular job duties, could be called to respond, or could be first on the scene at a technical rescue incident. At this level, the responder is generally not considered a rescuer.

Operations   The responder at this level should be capable of hazard recognition, equipment use, techniques necessary to perform shore- and boat-based rescues, and participate in a technical rescue under the supervision of technician level personnel.

Technician   A rescuer capable of hazard recognition, equipment use, and techniques to coordinate, perform and supervise a technical rescue. This may involve search, rescue and/or recovery operations.

NFPA 1670 is aimed at organizations and not individuals. However, by receiving training compliant to the standard, individuals will be an asset to their agency in meeting the overall standard requirements.

A complete copy of the standard can be purchased from www.nfpa.org.

NFPA 1006 – Standard for technical rescuer professional qualifications (revised 2017)

The purpose of the standard is to establish the minimum performance for emergency response personnel who perform technical rescue operations. To be compliant to the standard, the individual's performance must be assessed against the standard's criteria. In addition to the individual requirements, there are requirements placed on the AHJ, such as policy and procedure requirements.

A complete copy of the standard can be purchased from www.nfpa.org.

Rescue 3 International's training courses are compliant to the NFPA 1670 and 1006 standards. Training courses are provided at Awareness, Operations and Technician level, as well as skills-based assessments.

Other NFPA standards

NFPA 1670 and 1006 often reference other NFPA standards. This means personnel should also be conversant with the sections of the following that pertain to operations in, on, and near to swiftwater: NFPA 1500 Standard on Occupational Health and Safety; NFPA 1952 Standard on Surface Water Operations, Protective Clothing and Equipment; and NFPA 1983 Standard on Life Safety Rope and Equipment.

In the US

The following is a brief list of some of the more relevant standards for organizations with a swiftwater rescue responsibility in the United States:

Occupational Health and Safety Administration (OSHA) - Regulations that apply nationwide to emergency services, including regulations that specifically address surface and swiftwater rescue.

Federal Emergency Management Agency (FEMA) - Establishes emergency management plans and procedures that influence how state and local agencies respond to major swiftwater and flood incidents. Administers the National Incident Management System (NIMS).

Department of Homeland Security (DHS) - Administers FEMA & NIMS but also establishes a standardized typing system for resources used in emergency services. Also developing a National Emergency Services Credentialing System.

American Society for Testing and Materials (ASTM) - Conducts testing and develops standards for equipment used by emergency services.

American National Standards Institute (ANSI) - Assists in the development of standards relevant to rescue equipment.

State Legislation - Often includes legal requirements for emergency services that differ from state to state.

Local requirements - City or county policies, operating procedures and guidelines include emergency services.

In Canada

Occupational health and safety regulations in Canada are shared by 14 agencies: one federal, ten provincial, and three territorial. Provincial/territorial regulations apply in most cases, except for employees of the federal government, Crown agencies, and Crown corporations who are covered by federal legislation.

Provincial regulations contain little specifically related to working in, near, or on moving water but most provinces have guidelines that apply to the use of PFDs when there is a danger of drowning, and safety during work or travel on frozen bodies of water (lakes, ponds, rivers).

Federally, Transport Canada sets mandatory standards and regulations that apply to the use of boats for pleasure or work.

Rescue 3 Best Practice Guidelines

1

Rescue 3 has identified best practice guidelines to help students in developing an understanding of the basic principles of water rescue.

1 Keep it simple

Many rescues fail because rescue teams try to implement complicated solutions that take too long to set up or are above the ability level of the team members.

2 Always be proactive

As the oft-quoted proverb states, prevention is better than cure. Through effective education and risk mitigation, we can greatly reduce the potential of people becoming victims of water and floods, and thus reduce the need for rescues.

On-scene proactivity should be encouraged, by ensuring that there is a containment plan in place for the rescue scene. This means ensuring that there are upstream spotters and downstream safety/containment in place at a rescue scene, before any rescuers are committed to the water.

The person in charge should be proactive in thinking about alternative plans of action if the current plan fails. Each member of the team needs to observe the surroundings and think ahead.

3 Always operate within your capabilities and level of training

Rescuers should understand their remit and role. They should understand their own abilities, the abilities of their team, the equipment they have available, and the training that they have received. These should be evaluated alongside the environment that they are considering operating in.

There can be a lot of pressure on rescue teams to attempt a rescue, from family and bystanders and from the rescue team itself. There will be times where the rescue team are not equipped or trained for performing a rescue, and recognizing when a task is beyond the capability of the team is very important to ensure that team members and the victim are not put in further danger.

4 Self. Team. Victim.

The most important person at any rescue is yourself. Once you are in control of personal safety, then the next level of concern is for your fellow rescuers. Only after that can we begin to consider the victim. To the outsider, this may appear to be a self-centered and unfair approach. After all, is it not the victim that is in need of rescuing?

However, the victim can only be rescued by rescuers who are in control (and don't need rescuing themselves), and have the additional energy and ability to look after someone else as well as themselves. If a rescuer doesn't maintain their own safety, they are no longer a rescuer and become another victim. A team of rescuers who maintain individual and team safety will be a greater rescue asset to the casualty than an individual rescuer.

5 Always wear appropriate PPE

Anyone who is at risk of entering the water must be wearing appropriate PPE (Personal Protective Equipment) suitable for the environment they are working in. Generally this is defined as anyone who may be in the warm and hot zones.

6 Always use appropriate technical and team equipment

Water rescue equipment has progressed a long way in the past thirty years. There is no excuse for putting rescuers and victims at risk through the use of inappropriate, unsafe or improvised equipment if better alternatives are available. Equipment should be fit for purpose, compliant to any applicable standards, monitored and tested. Most importantly, rescuers must be familiar with the equipment they are using.

7 Always have a backup plan

The incident manager must always be looking at the bigger picture, thinking 'what if?' and 'what next?' Whilst team members are implementing Plan A, others need to be putting backup plans into operation. This may well require requesting additional resources and personnel, who need to be identified through a process of pre-planning.

Having downstream safety/containment in place is an important part of a backup plan, but it shouldn't be the only backup plan.

8 Never tie a rope around a rescuer

Rescuers have died as the result of being tied without a releasable system to a rope and then trapped underwater, unable to release themselves. If a rescuer is to enter the water attached to a rope, it must be attached to a specialist quick-release harness on a rescue PFD.

1 9 Never tension a rope at right angles to the current

When a rope is tensioned directly across the current and then loaded as a rescuer moves onto it, the water pressure will push the person downstream. The rope then forms a V in the downstream current with the rescuer at the downstream point of the V unable to move. Any rope tensioned across a river, should be at a minimum of 45° to the current vector, to enable swimmers to slide safely to the shore., See illustrations below.

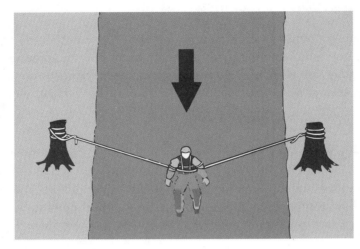

Never tension a rope at 90° to the current. As the swimmer comes onto the rope a downstream V is created, trapping them.

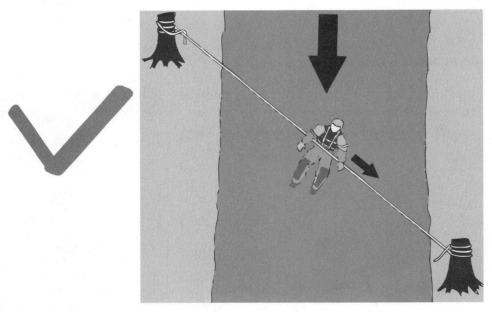

The rope should be tensioned at a minimum of 45° to the current, allowing the swimmer to slide down the rope to the bank.

10 Never stand downstream of, or inside a loop of rope

When operating with ropes around water, it is essential to be constantly vigilant to dangers created by the ropes. Standing in or on loops of rope on the bank puts the rescuer at risk of being trapped by the rope. Standing in loops created in a mechanical advantage system puts the rescuer at risk of being trapped, or hit by components of the system if the rope system fails.

When using ropes to anchor or recover objects in the water, or when a colleague is performing a throwbag rescue, rescuers need to stand on the upstream side of the rope. Then, as the object in the water moves downstream, the rescuer is not knocked over by the rope as it moves downstream.

11 Never put your feet down if swept away

Attempting to stand up in flowing water can lead to the potentially fatal situation of a foot entrapment. This is where a person's foot is trapped on the river bed, so the force of water pushes their body downstream and their head is pushed under the water. Foot entrapments can also be caused by underwater debris and hazards in flooded areas.

Correct use of swimming techniques, and not standing up until located in a safe eddy will greatly reduce the risk of foot entrapments.

Foot entrapment sequence

1 12 Choose rescue techniques according to the ability of the victim.

Victims may not be able to help in their own rescue.

Sometimes a simple throwbag or 'conditional rescue' is the fastest and most effective rescue, but exposure to the rapid cooling effects of water sometimes means that the victim is unable to assist in their own rescue.

If a victim is unlikely to be able to assist, rescue teams should utilize 'true rescue' techniques, that do not require the victim to assist in their own rescue

Communications

Often the difference between success and failure is effective communication.

For an incident to run smoothly, it is essential that there is a method of communication between all members of a team, and between the Incident Commander and the team.

This may be done simply, by voice or signaling to each other. However, there are many more technical methods such as a hand held radio system. If a technical method of communication is relied upon, it is imperative that a backup method is immediately available. Rescuers should remember that radios can break, and batteries can run flat. Reliance upon a single method of communication is dangerous.

Whatever method is used, it is essential that all team members recognize and understand it. Where necessary, the message should be shown back to confirm understanding. Often the river bank is a noisy environment and not conducive to good communication. So it is vital that communications are clear, concise and understood by all.

Hand signals

The diagrams below shows commonly accepted hands signals

One hand on top of head: Okay

One hand extended above the head: Distress (US/Europe)
Attention (Canada)

1

Pointing above the horizontal:
move in that direction

Both arms crossed in front of chest: Need medical help

Palm shown: Stop

Hand signals – moving a boat

Point positively: Move the boat in that direction

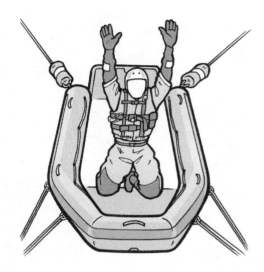

Both hands raised: Stop (US/Europe)
Both hands raised or waiving: Help! (Canada)

Whistle signals

1 blast	Stop or attention
2 blasts	Attention upstream or move upstream
3 blasts	Attention downstream or move downstream
3 blasts repeated	Emergency or rescue

Radios

Where handheld radios are to be used, communications should be disciplined and structured to avoid cluttering the airwaves. This helps to avoid missing important messages.

To prevent damage and to ensure the radios are kept operational, they should be kept in a waterproof case that they can be operated in. Water-resistant and waterproof radios are available, although care should be taken not to exceed the rated limits.

2 HYDROLOGY

Merced River, Yosemite National Park, California

Photo: Julie Munger

2

SECTION CONTENTS

Hydrology

Moving water

2

One inch of rain falling over one square mile produces 17.38 million gallons of water (or 430,000 bath tubs full) of water all traveling towards the lowest point[1].

In metric terms, 1cm of rain falling over 1km² produces 10,000,000 litres of water, all traveling towards the lowest point.

Moving water has three key characteristics. It is:

Powerful   Moving water exerts a force on any objects it impacts upon, whether they are cars, rocks, bridges or people in the water. This force is dependent upon the speed of the water. As the speed of the current increases, so does the power. See page 26 for more information.

Relentless   Moving water will exert a continuous force on an object. This is unlike an ocean wave which has a cycle of breaking and receding.

Predictable   Moving water may look very random, but to the trained eye it is orderly and predictable. Surface features can be read and used to predict what is happening under the water.

Rescue 3 Definitions of Water

Basic   Typically still, flat water, e.g., lakes, ponds, canals.

Moving   Water flowing down a gradient, e.g., streams, rivers, drainage, or channels

Coastal   Water located in sea, ocean or estuaries

Swiftwater   Fast moving water, flowing down a steeper gradient, e.g., steep rivers, drainage channels, flash flood conditions.

Whitewater   Fast moving water, flowing down a steeper gradient, used for recreational purposes, eg steep rivers for kayaking, canoeing, and whitewater rafting.

NFPA Definition of Swiftwater

The NFPA defines Swift Water as "Water moving at a rate greater than one knot [1.15 mph (1.85 km/hr)]" (NFPA 1670, 2017).

---

1 USGS Water Science Center http://water.usgs.gov/edu/earthrain.html

Channel characteristics

The nature of the rivers and floods are variable, and determined by four main factors:

- The volume of water flowing
- The channel gradient
- The nature of the channel bed and banks
- The water speed

By understanding how moving water behaves, we can use that knowledge, and by doing so avoid unnecessary or unacceptable levels of danger.

Volume

By knowing the measurements of a channel at any spot, we can calculate its present flow volume at any point between confluences.

Flow volume is measured in cubic feet per second (cf/s) often referred to as 'cfs', or cubic meters per second (cms)

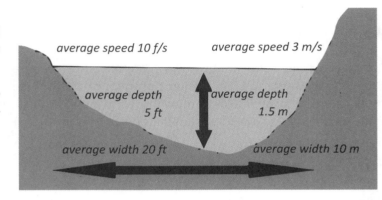

average speed 10 f/s   *average speed 3 m/s*

average depth 5 ft   *average depth 1.5 m*

average width 20 ft   *average width 10 m*

Using the graphic opposite as an example:

Depth	x	Width	x	Speed	=	Volume
5 ft	x	20 ft	x	10 f/s	=	1000 cfs
1.5 m	x	10 m	x	3 m/s	=	45 m³/s

The channel is carrying 1000 cubic feet per second (or 45 cubic meters per second), everywhere between the first confluence above where the river was measured and the first confluence below.

One cubic foot of water is approximately 8 gallons of water and there are approximately 250 gallons of water in 1 ton. Thus 1000 cubic feet of water per second equates to 8,000 gallons of water per second, or 32 tons of water per second.

One cubic meter of water is 1,000 liters of water and 1,000 kg. Thus 45 cubic meters of water per second equates to 45,000 liters of water per second, or 45 tons of water per second.

Channel gradient

Generally, channel gradient is the main determining factor on water speed. As a general guide, the steeper the channel water is flowing down, the higher the water speed will be. The gradient profile is also a critical factor. A gradient of 100 feet (30.5 meters) over 1 mile (1.6 km) could be a uniform slope with high water speed, or a series of slow moving pools divided by four 25 foot (7.6 m) waterfalls.

Nature of the channel bed and banks

The type of channel bed and banks will have significant input in determining a number of factors such as water speed and hazards.

Smooth-sided, man-made drainage channels can result in very uniform flows and little entrapment risk. They can create very high flow speeds, which can make rescue difficult. A straight-running drainage channel will have much higher water speeds than a natural river channel of the same gradient. Water colliding with the banks of the channel will create helical flow, thus also tending to push debris or people back towards the middle of the channel.

Natural river beds vary greatly depending upon the rock type and resultant morphology, and can present significant risk of foot entrapment at low water, or flush drowning at higher water flows.

Water speed

The speed of the water will be mainly determined by the three factors above. Constrictions in channels will also increase water speed. The volume of water cannot be altered, so if the channel is constricted then either the water depth or speed (or both) will need to increase. Such situations occur both in natural river channels (mid-stream rocks) and in flood situations (walls, cars in streets).

Force of water

The relationship between the speed of moving water and the force it exerts is not a linear one. Instead, the force[2] increases by the square of the speed. For example, if the speed of the water doubles, the force that the water exerts on an object is quadrupled.

Current velocity	Approximate force on legs	Approximate force on body
3mph - 4.8km/h - 1.3m/s Walking pace	**75N** **17 lbf**	**150N** **34 lbf**
6mph - 9.7km/h - 2.7m/s Steady jog	**300N** **67 lbf**	**600N** **134 lbf**
9mph - 14.5km/h - 4.0m/s Run	**675N** **151 lbf**	**1,350N** **302 lbf**
12mph - 19.3km/h - 5.4m/s Fast run	**1,200N** **269 lbf**	**2,400N** **537 lbf**

Rounded figures are based upon research carried out by the Ohio Department of Natural Resources in 1980.

---

2   Force is measured in Newtons. A mass of 1kg being acted upon by gravity will exert a force of approximately 10 Newtons (symbol N) on the surface it is resting upon. Therefore, the force on the legs in 3mph (4.8 km/h) water is equivalent to a mass of 16.5 lbs (7.5kg) resting on the legs.

Recent research by the Flood Hazard Research Centre[3] on human stability in flowing water has provided some more robust data to support the Ohio DNR[4] data.

A flow of approximately 7.2 mph (11.6 km/h) can start to wash people off their feet in a depth of only 9-10 inches (22.5-25.5 cm) of water (shin height).

In water approximately 3 feet deep (1 meter) (waist depth), flows of 2.2 mph (3.5 km/h) become challenging, and by approximately 4 mph (6.5 km/h) everybody will be washed off their feet.

Of course, these approximations will vary depending upon the height and weight of the individual, their clothing, the bottom composition and so on.

Transportation of loads

Rivers and water courses carry loads in a variety of ways. Water rescue personnel should be alert to hazards and debris flowing beneath the surface.

Top load or surface load

This will include kayaks, rafts and floating debris such as sticks. The top load will also contain swimmers and victims with PFDs.

Suspended load

Suspended loads travel under the surface, and are difficult to detect. This will include debris that is waterlogged such as trees, sinking vehicles etc. Dead bodies are also likely to travel as a suspended load (depending on the state of decomposition).

Bottom load

The bottom load contains heavy objects that will be pushed or rolled along the river bottom. In high energy water, this could include boulders rolling along the bottom, vehicles etc.

Dissolved load

The dissolved load is hazardous material and chemicals that have mixed in with the water. These solutions may not have been diluted to the point of no longer being harmful.

---

3   www.fhrc.mdx.ac.uk

4   www.dnr.state.oh.us

Flowing water hydrology

River orientation

2

Upstream   The direction that the water is flowing from.

Downstream   The direction that the water is flowing to.

River right   The right side of the channel when looking downstream.

River left   The left side of the channel when looking downstream.

An important thing to remember is that 'river right', and 'river left' are always set relating to the flow of the water, and not the viewer's perspective.

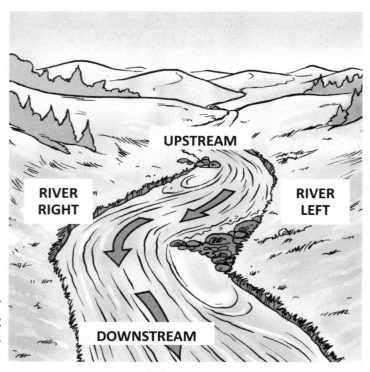

Flow types

There are two types of current flows encountered in moving water channels.:

Laminar flow

All the water in a channel does not travel at the same speed. Layers of water in contact with the channel bed and sides are slowed down by the effects of friction. The water closer to the middle is slowed down by friction against the slower water. The fastest flow is in the center of the channel, just below the surface – furthest from the bank.

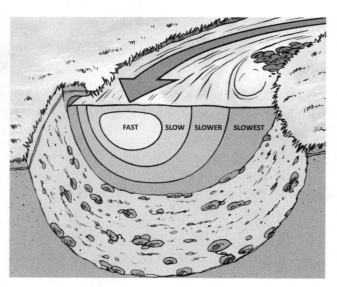

Helical flow

This is a spiraling effect caused by the banks slowing down the water at the edge of the river and the faster movement of mid-channel water. It is a relatively unusual feature along the banks in natural channels, unless they are full to the top, and traveling at their maximum speed. Helical flow can, however, be noticed in other areas, such as eddy lines.

The helical flow can push a victim and river debris away from the bank into the center of the river.

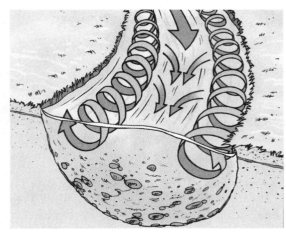

Current vector

Current vector is the technical term for the direction in which the water is flowing. Moving water follows the path of least resistance, flowing in a straight line, unless acted upon by an external force or object.

Water at point A is flowing in a straight line, until it hits the bank at point B. The water then follows the bank around until it reaches the apex at point C, where it carries on in a straight line until it hits the bank again at point D and follows that bank around. Water follows the path of least resistance, and so will always try to fill an empty vessel, such as an eddy at point E.

As a result, the current creates high pressure areas on the outside of bends. This can cause erosion, leading to undercut banks. Conversely, there will be low pressure areas on the inside of bends. This can lead to deposition or shallow water on the inside of bends.

An awareness and understanding of current vector is essential for personnel to be able to successfully self-rescue, and to perform rescues. A clear reading of the current vector will enable rescuers to work with the force of the river (where possible) rather than against it.

Flowing water features

Terminology and definitions

2

River bed and channel-side features can create many water features. The type of feature created by objects and obstructions is generally determined by the water level and speed.

Eddy

Behind the eddy fence, on the downstream side of the rock, is the eddy. As there is a high pressure area (the cushion wave) on the upstream side of the object, there must be a low pressure area on the downstream side of the object.

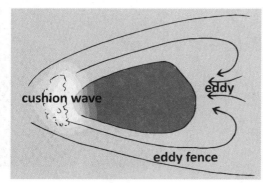

The water in this lower pressure area will be flowing upstream. This is known as an eddy current. Eddy currents are normally slower than the main current and appear as an area of calmer water. While they are normally areas of relative safety, some powerful eddy currents can create dangerous eddies that can be difficult to enter due to the eddy fence.

Eddy line (eddy fence)

This is a boundary line in a river where the water currents move in opposite directions on each side. The difference between the eddy and the main downstream flow ranges from gentle surface ripples to deep recirculation.

Upstream V

After the water has hit the object and created the cushion wave, it then flows around either side of the object. This creates a V-shaped feature when seen from above, and the point of the V is upstream. This is known as an upstream V. Any time that an upstream V is present, there is an obstruction, even if the object itself is not visible.

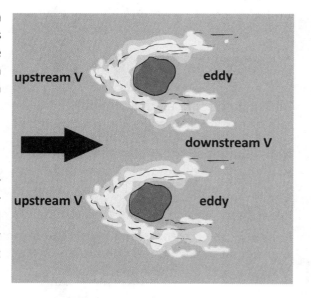

Downstream V

If there is more than one object in the flow, then water will be forced between the objects. This flow of water can be identified by a V shape pointing downstream, and is known as a downstream V. This feature is caused by the convergence of water flow into the channel of least resistance and generally indicates the deepest channel.

Picture of a Downstream V

Cushion wave

A cushion wave is created when the water hits an object that it cannot pass through. As the water cannot pass through, it bounces off the object before passing to either side of it. This is an area of high pressure. If an object does not appear to be creating a cushion wave, then the water is either passing through it (like a strainer, see page 35), or underneath it (like a siphon, see page 34)

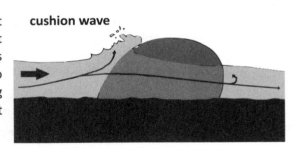

Standing wave

As the water level increases, the object is submerged deep underwater, and the water must pass over and around each side of the object. This can cause waves to be created on the surface of the water. These can be large, steep waves with breaking tops (haystack waves) or gentle surface waves. This depends upon the speed of the water, and the size of the underwater object in relation to the depth of the water. A series of standing waves is known as a wave train.

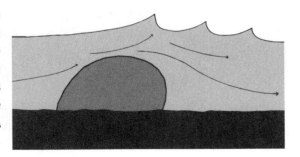

Hydraulics

If the water level is at the point where the water is flowing over an object, the water feature changes again.

Hydraulics come in many different shapes and sizes, but are created when water flows over an object and accelerates down the downstream side. This creates a depression downstream of the object, which the water flows back into creating a recirculation.

Recirculations can be dangerous as they can be powerful enough to hold objects such as debris, boats and swimmers.

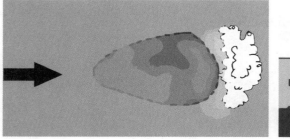 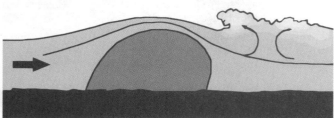

Aerial and profile view of water flowing over a rock to create a hydraulic

It is possible to determine how dangerous a hydraulic is. This is normally based on the physical features of the hydraulic:

Height of the drop

The higher the drop, the more speed the water gains as it falls, which means more energy within the hydraulic. This energy is manifested within the recirculation and within the water flowing downstream beneath the recirculation (outflow). How much is within the recirculation and how much is within the outflow is determined by the slope of the drop.

Slope of the drop (face)

A steep angle forces the water down towards the river bed, creating a deep recirculation with little downstream outflow. A shallow angle creates more of a surface recirculation with more downstream outflow. Deep recirculations tend to be more powerful with a greater holding potential, and are, consequently, a greater hazard.

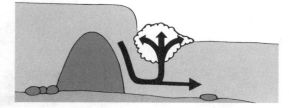 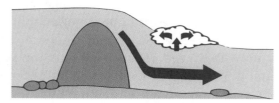

Full depth recirculation   *Surface recirculation*

Towback (Backwash)

The towback is the water at the surface of the recirculation that is flowing back upstream towards the hydraulic (it is called the towback or backwash as it tows debris etc back into the hydraulic). The downstream edge of the towback is indicated by the boil line - the point where the water resurfaces and either flows back into the hydraulic or downstream. The distance of the towback is measured from the face of the hydraulic to the boil line; the greater the towback, the greater the hazard. At the boil line, if there is more water flowing back into the towback than there is flowing downstream, this may indicate a more powerful recirculation with a strong towback.

Shape

Naturally-formed hydraulics within rivers tend to have an irregular shape, with an associated irregular recirculation. This can create weaknesses within the recirculation (flush points), where more water is flowing downstream. These can act as exit points for a swimmer.

A key factor within the shape of a hydraulic is where its most downstream point is. If it is one of its corners, this may provide an exit point. As water flows to the lowest/most downstream point, the water may feed to this corner and exit the recirculation. These are known as open corners. Anything entering the hydraulic may be fed to this point and exit the recirculation. It is possible for both ends of a hydraulic to be downstream, with two open corners.

If the corners of the hydraulic are the upstream point, these are closed corners - the water will flow away from them towards the center of the hydraulic. Closed corners may offer no exit and tend to present a greater hazard. Closed corners can also be formed by obstructions, such as rocks, or in the case of man-made lowhead dams, concrete walls, which prevent exit from the corners of the hydraulic.

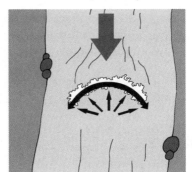
Open-cornered hydraulic

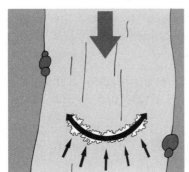
Closed-cornered hydraulic

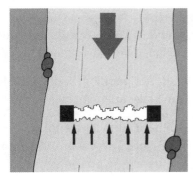
Closed-cornered hydraulic caused by obstructions

These factors determine the nature of the hydraulic and need to be considered when making an assessment. Another important factor is what will be exposed to a hydraulic: a boat and a swimmer have different buoyancy levels and will act differently in hydraulics. Even if one aspect is favorable, such as a short drop or small towback, other factors, such as closed corners, may still create a considerable hazard.

Physical hazards

In addition to generic hazards of moving water, there are a number of other common physical hazards.

Undercuts

2

An undercut rock or soil bank will often appear on the outside of a bend, where the current vector has worn it away. An undercut tends to lack a visible cushion wave, as the water will be traveling under the rock or soil rather than bouncing off it. Consequently, there is a significant risk of entrapment.

Siphons

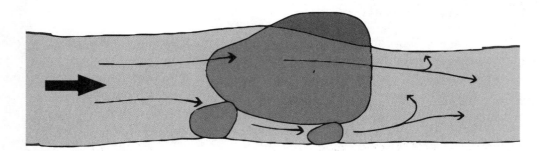

Water flowing under a partially supported object or vehicle creates a siphon

A siphon is formed when an object in the flow has a gap underneath it (for example, a boulder perched on a number of smaller rocks or a car in the water). This allows the water to flow underneath the object as well as around it. The water flowing under the boulder is siphoning. It is a very dangerous feature as it will cause objects (including swimmers) to be sucked down under the object, where they can potentially become trapped.

If water is siphoning under an object, there is generally a small cushion wave (see page 31) or even no cushion wave at all on its upstream side. This is a classic sign of a siphon being present under the water.

Cars on hard surfaces standing in the water are classic siphon-creating features. The car can sit on the river bed on its wheels. The water will siphon under the car, as well as travel around the car. This is a major hazard to anyone operating on the upstream side of the car.

Inspection "Manhole" covers

In a flooded environment, inspection (or manhole) covers and drain covers can become displaced by the upwelling water as the flood rises. When the floodwater starts to recede, these open holes then become incredibly dangerous and powerful siphons. The force exerted by these siphons is relentless, and very powerful – due to the physics of vortices. A simple wading pole is essential to locate uncovered inspection hatches and drains.

Bridges

Bridge abutments are normally designed to minimize forces from the water, and therefore may not have a cushion wave. This could make it easier to trap or pin a boat or unwary swimmer.

Debris

Any kind of natural or manufactured debris can find its way into the water. This can pose a hazard when traveling downstream into a rescue site. Debris can become an entrapment hazard. It can also collect on bridge abutments to form a strainer hazard.

Strainers

A strainer is anything that allows water to pass through it, but not solid objects such as debris, boats or swimmers. Common strainers include trees fallen into the water, fences, and railings. The force of the current will hold objects against the strainer indefinitely. The danger that strainers pose to rescuers cannot be understated. It is essential to ensure that any strainers on a rescue site are well protected, to minimize risks to rescue personnel. For more information on strainers, see page 113.

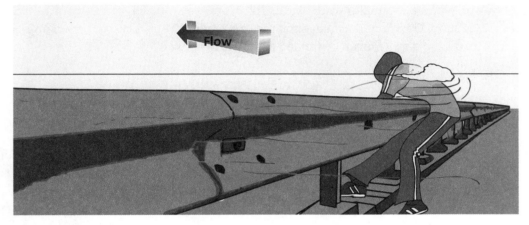

Commonplace structures, such as railings, can become a hazard in a flooded environment

Strainer

Cold water

Water removes heat from the human body much faster than air. Cold water will quickly sap even the strongest swimmer's strength. The dramatic effect of the cold water on the body cannot be overemphasized to a potential rescuer. For further information, see page 102.

Rivers are composed of natural and human introduced hazards. These hazards often interact to create a dynamic environment. Hazards must be continually re-evaluated as water levels change.

International River Classification Scale

2

The International River Classification Scale is a standardized scale to measure the technical difficulty of a particular section of river, and the skill level required to successfully navigate it. This is also known as the International River Grading Scale in some parts of the world. Rescuers should remember that this is a recreational scale and does not necessarily reflect how easy (or difficult) a rescue is to perform. Rescuers and victims have both drowned and been entrapped in Class 2 water.

Class I	Fast moving water with ripples and small waves. Few obstructions, all obvious and easily missed with training. Risk to swimmers is slight; self-rescue is easy.
Class II	Straightforward rapids with wide, clear channels, which are evident without scouting. Occasional maneuvering may be required, but rocks and medium-sized waves are easily missed by trained paddlers.
Class III	Rapids with moderate, irregular waves which may be difficult to avoid and which can swamp an open canoe. Complex maneuvers in fast current and good boat control in tight passages or around ledges are often required; large waves or strainers may be present but are easily avoided. Strong eddies and powerful current effects can be found, particularly on large volume rivers. Scouting is advisable for inexperienced parties. Injuries while swimming are rare; self-rescue is usually easy but group assistance may be required to avoid long swims.
Class IV	Intense, powerful but predictable rapids requiring precise boat handling in turbulent water. Depending on the character of the river, it may feature large, unavoidable waves and holes or constricted passages demanding fast maneuvers under pressure. Rapids may require 'must' moves above dangerous hazards. Scouting may be necessary the first time down. Risk of injury to swimmers is moderate to high, and water conditions may make self-rescue difficult. Group assistance for rescue is often essential but requires practiced skills.
Class V	Extremely long, obstructed, or very violent rapids which expose a paddler to added risk. Drops may contain large, unavoidable waves and holes or steep, congested chutes with complex, demanding routes. Rapids may continue for long distances between pools, demanding a high level of fitness. What eddies exist may be small, turbulent, or difficult to reach. At the high end of the scale, several of these factors may be combined. Scouting is recommended but may be difficult. Swims are dangerous, and rescue is often difficult even for experts.
Class VI	These runs have almost never been attempted and often exemplify the extremes of difficulty, unpredictability and danger. The consequences of errors are very severe and rescue may be impossible. For teams of experts only, at favorable water levels, after close personal inspection and taking all precautions.

Notes

3   FLOODING

Somerset levels flooding, UK   *Photo*: Devon and Somerset Fire and Rescue Service

3

SECTION CONTENTS

Flood theory

Although working in floods is essentially the same as working in any water environment, with all associated water hazards, it also has some specific issues.

River levels will vary greatly, depending upon factors such as rainfall, snowmelt, release from upstream dams etc. However, most of the time the river level will be within the river channel. Therefore, its flow and features are relatively predictable. As river levels rise, they will eventually reach a point where they are 'bankfull', so any subsequent rise will see the riverbanks overtopped and the water flowing through the adjacent low areas of land – the floodplain.

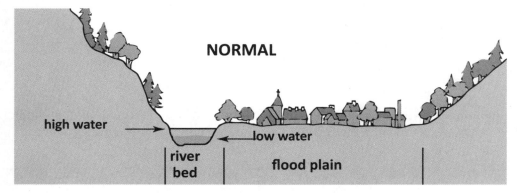

High and low water levels are normally contained within the banked channel

The increased volume of water means that most previously existing river hazards, such as lowhead dams, are probably now more powerful and dangerous, although some may actually become washed out. Additionally, there are now a range of new hazards. There may no longer be enough clearance under bridges for boats to pass. Water now flows through and around obstacles that were not designed to be in water and which create major hazards, for example parked cars, fences, hedges, gates, road signs, and park benches.

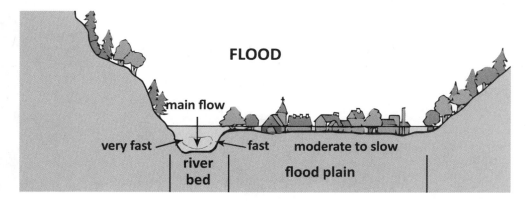

During a flood event, the water overtops the river banks and spreads onto the flood plain

Floodwater will be carrying large amounts of debris which can build up against houses and bridges and cause structural damage, as well as presenting significant risk to anyone in the water.

As water flows through the flood plain, the chance to become contaminated by hazardous materials, such as sewage, agricultural waste, and pesticides, is massively increased.

It is worth noting that once the water overflows the river banks and spreads across the flood plain, this may result in an apparent reduction in the speed of the water. However, the water flowing where the original river channel is will still be flowing at its previous rate. These all go towards making working in floods a hazardous and arduous task.

The four realities of flooding

Floods, by their very nature, are:

- Multi-agency events
- Multi-jurisdictional events
- Hazmat and public health events
- Long-term events that can exhaust emergency personnel and community members emotionally, mentally, and physically

Rescue teams and emergency planners must understand that floods have their own life, and specific requirements. With effective pre-planning, specific training and appropriate equipment for these incidents, members of the public will be better protected from the effects of flooding.

At any major flood event, there will be many agencies on scene. It is essential that these agencies communicate effectively, and work together efficiently.

Floodwater does not respect any authority, boundaries or jurisdictions. As a result, rescue teams will be working with teams from other areas. By establishing common training techniques and equipment, this mutual aid process can be greatly simplified.

The public health implications of large scale flooding are clear: large numbers of people will be exposed to contaminants. The very young and the very old are most at risk. Health services in the area will be stretched to capacity.

The long-term nature of flooding cannot be overstated. Irrespective of the amount of resources available, there will always be a requirement for more. Years after the rescue response has been completed, members of the public may still be living in temporary accommodation, waiting for their homes to be rebuilt and refurbished.

3

The four phases of flooding

Flood incidents may be broken down into four phases. Every flood will progress through these phases, although because each flood is unique, it will progress at a different speed.

Phase 1 – Pre-flood

Flooding has not yet occurred. However, it will at some point in the future. Now is the time to develop a response plan based on an existing hazard assessment that includes historical flood data. This is also a good time to train personnel and invest in equipment. Public education during this phase can be invaluable for when the flood event occurs.

Phase 2 – Flash flood

Streams, rivers, storm drains and waste water management systems are full. Water is just beginning to escape waterways, to cover roads, and to impact property.

This phase is associated with high speed water. Most technical rescues will occur during this phase. People are caught unawares and lives are in imminent danger. During this phase rescuers will be at their greatest personal risk.

Phase 3 – Expansion

Streams and rivers are now clearly out of their banks and the water is moving laterally. Land is now being lost significantly, which means that access and egress will also be compromised. This phase is evacuation-intensive since structures, regardless of their occupancies, are now impacted. As essential infrastructure is now being compromised, hazmat issues begin to surface.

Evacuation means that people can leave under their own power – which is often not the case here. If people are being moved by rescue teams (for example by boat), then rescues are taking place. The new term is 'rescue evacuation'. This consumes resources and time.

Phase 4 – Recovery

As property owners begin to return, agencies will note an increase in accidents and injuries due to newly exposed hazards. Structures and roads should be inspected. Infrastructure restoration and hazmat issues are now the most pressing. Due to hazmat issues, public health agencies will be very busy. Search and rescue work will stop, and turn to search and recovery.

The use of rescue resources (especially inflatable boats) must be adjusted due to the decreasing water levels and emergence of new hazards. Emergency personnel should be closely monitored for fatigue, and the personal losses they may have suffered.

Flood return predictions

Floods are often referred to as the 'one in a hundred year flood'. This does not mean that they will occur every hundred years, but rather there is a 1 in 100 or 1% chance of such a flood occurring every year. A 'one in two hundred year flood' represents a 1 in 200 or 0.5% chance of the floodwaters reaching that height in any given year. It is even possible for two 'one in hundred year' floods to occur on the same river in the same year or even the same month. Looking at historic flood data and river flow measurements allows for computer models to be developed which can be used to produce flood return statistics and produce detailed flood mapping.

Flood mapping

The ability to look into the future to see how many city blocks and roads might be flooded in a few days is becoming clearer with Flood Inundation Mapping. Sets of maps (referred to as libraries) are being developed which show both the extent and depth of water for various flood levels ranging from minor flooding all the way through to record flood levels. These new flood prediction tools help emergency managers and impacted citizens be better prepared to make important decisions regarding evacuations, moving property, and other mitigation efforts.

Combined with traditional forecasts and flood bulletin information, these new flood maps show the areas of likely inundation based on current conditions and future rainfall. Maps are produced using geographic information systems (GIS) and data gathered for Flood Insurance Rate Maps.

In the US, the National Oceanic and Atmospheric Administration's (NOAA) National Weather Service (NWS) and its National Ocean Service (NOS) Coastal Services Center (CSC) work in collaboration with the Federal Emergency Management Agency (FEMA) and other partners to develop inundation maps for both coastal and inland freshwater flooding.

North of the border, Environment Canada and a network of affiliates in each province provide the same service.

In the UK, flood maps are available on the Environment Agency's website2. By entering a postcode, it is possible to see a map of flood areas and flood defenses. The Environment Agency maps can be viewed in up to 1:10,000 scale. The maps show levels based on 1 in 100 year events for rivers, 1 in 200 year events for coastal flooding, as well as 1 in 1,000 year events.

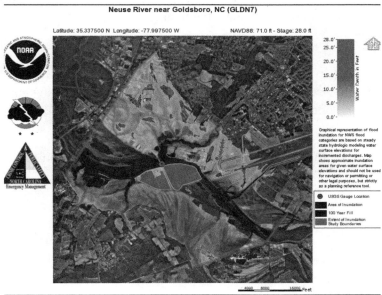

NOAA flood inundation map for the Nuese River, Goldboro, NC.

Flood warnings and alerts

Accurate warnings of predicted flood events are a vital tool. Warnings allow for the implementation of pre-planned responses including evacuations, placement of flood defences, initiation of road closures and pre-deployment of search and rescue resources.

In the next section we'll take a look at two systems on different continents to see how they are being put to use to keep the people in their jurisdiction safe.

European Flood Alert System

The European Flood Alert System (EFAS) provides flood alert information directly to national authorities. Their website at www.efas.eu/national-information.html provides links to national and regional authorities that publish publicly-available flood forecasts.

In the UK, for example, the Environment Agency operates a warning system called Floodline. This has a series of warning codes, which are:

FLOOD ALERT

Flood Alert means that flooding is possible and that the public should be prepared. It is used between two hours and two days in advance of forecast flooding.

- Be prepared to act upon your flood plan.
- Prepare a flood kit of essential items.
- Monitor local water levels and flood forecasts.

FLOOD WARNING

Flood Warning means that flooding is expected, and immediate action is required. It is used between half an hour and one day in advance of flooding.

- Move family, pets and valuables to a safe place.
- Turn off gas, electricity, and water supplies if safe to do so.
- Put flood protection equipment into place.

SEVERE FLOOD WARNING

Severe Flood Warning means that there is severe flooding and danger to life. It is used when flooding poses a significant threat to life.

- Stay in a safe place with means of escape.
- Be ready should you need to evacuate your home.
- Co-operate with the emergency services.
- Call 999/112 if you are in immediate danger.

When no further flooding is expected, and river and sea conditions are going back to normal, there will be no warnings in force.

This information is available via a freephone telephone number (0845 988 1188) or the internet. If flood warnings are in place, this fact is often reported on TV and radio weather forecasts.

It is also possible for householders and businesses in high risk areas to register with Floodline Warnings Direct - a free service from the Environment Agency that provides flood warnings direct to you by telephone, mobile, email, SMS, and fax.

FINS

In the United States, there are some excellent examples of systems which link flood early warning systems directly to the Emergency Services. The Flood Information and Notification System (FINS) in operation in Charlotte, North Carolina is a particularly good example.

FINS is not intended to be a public warning system. It only notifies emergency responders. The National Weather Services provides Flood Watches and Flood Warnings to the news media and public.

FINS alerts local fire, police, medics, and emergency management to the threat or actual danger of flooding.

FINS is a partnership involving the City of Charlotte, Mecklenburg County and the US Geological Survey. They continually monitor rainfall and stream depth levels. Emergency responders are notified when there is a potential or actual problem.

Three levels of FINS

Alert

When rainfall is intense or streams rise rapidly, the FINS system automatically sends the alert via pager, mobile phone and email to emergency responders and Storm Water Services staff.

Investigate

If the situation gets worse, emergency personnel must personally visit the location of heavy rainfall or flooding. They will barricade streets or take other action if needed.

Emergency

The highest level. Additional precautions may be necessary, such as evacuating residents near the high-water areas.

For more information, see http://finslive.mecklenburgcountync.gov

Floodwater dynamics and hazards

The ability to recognize and risk assess swiftwater and flood hazards is a vital skill. Each hazard must be identified and addressed before performing a rescue. There is an enormous variety of hazards in a moving water and flood environment. A small selection is outlined below:

Utility hazards

Electricity

Clearly, electricity and water do not mix. Power lines may short out or arc. During flooding, the height between the power lines and surface is reduced - this of particular importance during boat operations.

Substations can be flooded, leading to wide areas without electricity. Utilities companies should identify infrastructure at risk of flooding, and, ideally, a detailed response plan that provide protection for the infrastructure that will be in place.

Although power may be out in an area, some establishments have a backup or emergency system. This information should be in the agency pre-plan.

Natural gas

Gas mains can be ruptured if the earth around the pipe is eroded by floodwater. If houses are damaged then domestic piping can be ruptured, resulting in leaking gas. Clearly, this poses a significant fire hazard and an explosion hazard, particularly if operating powerboats.

LPG and oil tanks

As the contents of these tanks is lighter than water, even when they are full, they are buoyant. As tanks become immersed, they can break free of their framework and float off, venting gas or spilling oil.

Chemical and biological hazards

All waterways are polluted to some degree. Floodwater can contain significant amounts of hazardous material (hazmat). This may be industrial waste, sewage effluent, fuel, agricultural chemicals, dead animals, and much more washed into the water. These pollutants can cause serious health problems to people working near or in the water.

Personal hygiene is important while working near the water and personnel should be decontaminated following possible exposure. For more information on decontamination, see page 102.

Possible hazmat locations

3

Urban

- Fuel and oil from flooded vehicles
- Sewers
- Storm drains
- Fuel storage tanks
- Chemical bunds
- Household waste
- Industrial chemicals

Rural

- Pesticides
- Fertilizers
- Slurry pits
- Septic tanks
- Dead animals

Working in floods

Although a flood is a water incident and there are many similarities with dealing with a typical water rescue, there are also differences when dealing with flooding.

Early command and control needs to be established and maintained. Incident command is vital to communicate, plan, allocate, control, brief and debrief the many multi-agency teams that may be involved.

Consideration must be given to weather conditions, particularly current rainfall, predicted rainfall, tidal influences and land drainage. Clearly, these factors will all influence the water level. This continual change will affect the type of approach rescuers take to a situation. As the water level changes, so may the water speed, which could greatly affect operations.

Floodwater can be very changeable with regards to depth, flow, speed, and volume. Generally, these rates can be predicted by relevant agencies who can give an approximation of expected water levels.

Hazards

Floodwater can be flowing and moving in places it was never intended to be. Once rivers overspill their defined channels and interact with the wider environment, there is a whole new set of physical, biological and chemical hazards to deal with. Rescuers need to be constantly looking out for new hazards.

Floodwater is almost certainly contaminated. It is possible that the water has come up through the sewer system, and has been contaminated with chemicals or contains petrochemicals. Consideration should be given to such issues as testing and sampling of the water, and decontamination of personnel, equipment, and PPE. All floods should be treated as hazardous material incidents, and suitable decontamination processes should be adopted. The health of personnel exposed to floodwater should be monitored. For further information on decontamination, see page 102.

Equipment

Where personnel are committed to the water as a wading response, they should be appropriately dressed in drysuit, PFD and helmet. If waders are to be used instead of drysuits, consideration should be given to the possibility of the wearer stepping down into a deeper area of water and becoming immersed, from which it can be very difficult to recover. In addition, the skin will be contaminated with floodwater which may result in infection and illness.

All personnel operating in flooded areas should be issued with a suitable wading pole to allow them to check for underwater hazards. For more specific information, see page 114.

Tactics

Many bank-based rescue techniques can have limited applications in floods, due to the potential for wide areas of water. The effective use of both motor and paddle boats are a critical flood response asset. These require specialist training both to allow crew to operate the boat in a flowing water environment and to apply bank-based techniques such as throwbag and swimming rescues from these boats. Such training is available through the Rescue 3 Swiftwater and Flood Rescue Boat Operator (SFRBO) and Swiftwater Paddle Boat Handling (SPBH) courses.

If boats are being used, then the choice of boat type will be an issue. For more information on boat types, see page 68. When the water is deep and fast-flowing, powered inflatable boats work well. When the water becomes shallow, it may be necessary to use hard-bottomed boats. Rescuers may be able to wade in the water with boats to perform rescues. However, if the flow is too fast or the depth variable, then more advanced rescue techniques will be required, such as an aerial rope rescue or a helicopter.

Evacuation

Many people may need rescuing from a flooded area. Not all of these will be technical rescues. Incident managers need to decide who is to be rescued first and which rescue teams are best capable to deal with individual incidents – team typing is of a great help here.

Where rescuers are moving large amounts of people, consideration should be given to how they will be transported. Personal flotation devices in a full range of sizes, from small child to XXL adult, will be needed for members of the public. These should be clearly marked and a different color from those used by responders.

During an evacuation, people will need advice about what personal possessions they can realistically bring with them. Family pets can be problematic to deal with – many people refuse to leave without their pets and accommodation for pets should be available. The PETS Act authorizes FEMA to provide rescue, shelter, and essential needs for individuals with household pets and service animals, and to the household pets and animals themselves following a major flood disaster[1]. People who have been rescued will need help and advice about emergency shelter and accommodation.

Search

Search is a major consideration in flood events. Not all victims will be obvious. House to house searches are required to ensure nobody is left trapped. These can be time-consuming and require many personnel to conduct them effectively. Once an area is searched, it should be marked according to international standards, and the incident management team informed, to avoid replication of work. This is usually done with spray paint on the outside of the property, on an area which will not cause undue damage, such as the door or roof.

3

1https://www.avma.org/KB/Resources/Reference/disaster/Pages/PETS-Act-FAQ.aspx

4   RESCUE EQUIPMENT AND SAFETY

Water rescue equipment, Evinos river, Greece

Photo: Rescue 3 Greece/Kayak Metavasi

4

SECTION CONTENTS

Personal equipment

Rescue teams carry a vast range of equipment, depending on their areas and levels of operation. Awareness level personnel are not rescue team members, but do need to have knowledge of the equipment used as they may perform a supporting role in the cold zone (see page 172).

4

Helmet

Whistle

PFD with integral quick release chest harness (knife in pocket)

Throwbag on quick release belt

Gloves

Drysuit with integral socks

Appropriate footwear (not integral boots)

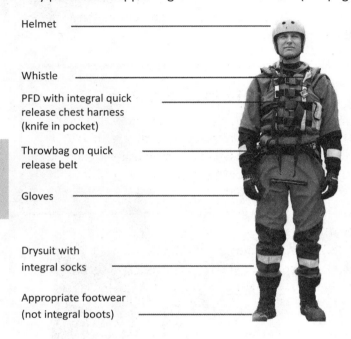

Rescue personnel need to be properly equipped for the situations they face and the role they intend to perform.

Protective clothing suitable for the task is essential. Just as firefighters would not wear a drysuit to attend a fire, the same approach must be adopted for water rescue. Fireproof clothing is unsuitable to enter the water.

Before equipment is chosen, it is necessary to look at the hazards that personnel need protection from. This directly relates to the zones to be operated in. In a water rescue, the most obvious hazard is the water itself. However, the hazmat issues of water rescue, and in particular flood events, must also be taken into consideration.

Personal protective equipment for a Rescue Technician

Drysuits

Personal protective equipment (PPE) must protect the wearer from the water itself and contact with it. A barrier is required between people and the hazardous material. A drysuit fulfills this purpose. A drysuit will fit a range of people, as long as the seals fit effectively.

A drysuit (membrane surface suit) offers a barrier but no impact protection or thermal properties. Therefore, a drysuit requires additional thermal clothing to be worn underneath. This can be regulated and layers added or taken away depending on the conditions.

Many different styles of drysuits are available. Some have integral boots and others offer gortex socks, latex socks or latex ankle seals.

Integral boots have the advantage of being complete and easily put on. The feet are protected from hazmat. The sizing of the boot is important for effective use. However, many boots tend to be difficult to swim in effectively, or they have soles which do not offer much grip. Integral boots cannot be removed if the boot is caught in an underwater entrapment. The drysuit would have to be compromised by cutting off the boot.

Possibly a better option is to use integral socks on the drysuit and have separate functional boots such as specialist water rescue boots, hiking boots or industrial safety boots. This option allows greater flexibility with equipment. Separate boots can then be the correct size for the end user. Naturally, latex socks are more fragile than integral boots and need to be protected more cautiously.

Wetsuits

Neoprene wetsuits offer good insulation and impact protection. Neoprene offers increased buoyancy for rescue swimmers. However to provide the best thermal qualities, wetsuits need to fit tightly. This makes them quite specific to individuals. Wetsuits work by trapping a layer of water between the individual's skin and the suit material which then becomes warm from the body heat. While wetsuits can be a good option for rescue teams when operating in clean rivers, they are not suitable for use in a flood environment as they offer no protection from hazmat, as the skin is in contact with the floodwater.

Personal flotation device (PFD)

A personal flotation device is any device which assists a person to float. Lifejackets (inflatable PFDs) and buoyancy aids are both different types of PFDs.

> **Terminology Note:**
>
> It is important to note that in the United States, the term PFD is used in common usage to denote both lifejackets and buoyancy aids.

4

PFDs For Rescuers

The most critical piece of equipment for anyone within 10 feet of the edge of the water is a good rescue buoyancy aid (PFD). Buoyancy aids are designed for intentional water entry, so are easy to swim in. They offer good impact protection as they are foam-filled. They also offer reasonably good insulation, but this is a negative when operating in the heat.

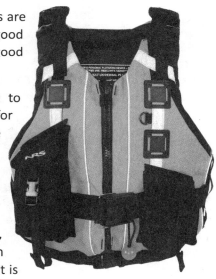

Rescue buoyancy aids have a number of extra functions in addition to providing buoyancy. They are highly visible. They provide storage for equipment and attachment for a knife. They also have a quick-release chest harness designed for work in the water environment. The harness is the only safe point to attach a floating rope to a rescuer. The quick-release chest harness is releasable under load, if the rescuer needs to escape the system.

A cowstail is a very useful addition to the quick-release chest harness, as it allows an individual rescuer to attach and detach themselves from rope systems with ease. However, the cowstail can pose a snag hazard if it is incorrectly stowed.

Fit is Key

While proper buoyancy is critical, fit is also very important when selecting a PFD. Try to find one that provides the proper flotation while still fitting properly. Comfort is important too, because if it is uncomfortable, it won't get worn.

Testing a Flotation Device

1. Try it on and fasten all the buckles and straps. Make sure you can breathe easily.

2. If you can pull it over your head, it's too big. If you can't fasten all the buckles and straps comfortably, it's too small.

3. With supervision, enter the water and float on your back. Make sure your chin clears that water so that you can breathe. If your chin/mouth is underwater, you need more flotation.

4. Try swimming on your front and back. Make sure you can move well enough and that your PFD or lifejacket does not float up around your face. If so, it's too big.

Specific Legislation

United States

In the United States, all PFDs are approved by the U.S. Coast Guard. The USCG recommends the following PFDs for emergency responders:

- Type III - for boat-based activity in calm, inland waters
- Type V - for special uses and work purposes
- Type III/V - multipurpose jackets that fit criteria of Type III & V

However, many PFDs in the above categories will not necessarily meet the minimum requirement for 22 lbs. of flotation set by the NFPA for surface water rescue. Check the label before you buy.

Europe

Buoyancy aids must conform to EN ISO 12402 parts 5 or 6 which replaces EN 393. Part 5 covers general buoyancy aids with a minimum buoyancy of 50N. Specialist buoyancy aids, including those with quick-release chest harnesses suitable for water rescue operations, are covered in part 6 of this standard.

Canada

In Canada, it's not so simple. All regulations regarding the design and approval of lifejackets and PFDs are under the federal authority of Transport Canada and cite standards developed by the Underwriters Laboratory (UL) and Canadian General Standards Board (CGSB). However, until recently, this was administered by the Canadian Coast Guard, and so some approved flotation devices may still carry Coast Guard labeling.

In addition, PFDs are only approved for use in pleasure craft in Canada. This is a problem because in our opinion, no approved lifejacket is suitable for use in swiftwater. So what does a responsible employer recommend for their personnel? We believe that given the fact that Transport Canada also categorizes work boats as pleasure craft if they are under 8 m in length and operated within sheltered waters one mile or less from shore that PFDs are also approved for work in these situations. But that is just our assumption and, to our knowledge, it has never been tested in court.

This assumption is given added weight because the use of lifejackets or PFDs for work is covered by provincial occupational health and safety legislation, and in British Columbia, for example, PFDs that meet the following standard are approved for work:

CGSB Standard CAN/CGSB-65.11-M88, Personal Flotation Devices with a minimum buoyancy of 69 N (15.5 lbs).

Worth noting however, is that the majority of lifejackets and PFDs sold (and worn) in Canada are made in the US and do not meet Canadian requirements for use on boats. And so the confusion grows.

We recommend what qualifies as either a Type III or Type IV PFD in the US.

- Type III PFDs - for those who work in, on or near moving water but for whom rescue is not their primary mandate
  » inherently buoyant (ie. not inflatable)
  » minimum buoyancy of 15.5 lbs
  » at least 2 cinch straps to ensure PFD stays in place in swiftwater
  » cinch-type strap and closure at the waist of the PFD

- Type V PFDs - for those whose primary mandate is rescue from swiftwater
  » inherently buoyant
  » minimum buoyancy of 15.5 lbs
  » at least 2 cinch straps to ensure PFD stays in place in swiftwater
  » cinch-type strap and closure at the waist of the PFD
  » quick-release system for tethering or towing

We stand behind our recommendations because accident data clearly shows that the increased use of PFDs has resulted in significantly reduced fatalities overall.[1]

In summary, it is up to the employer to determine how to navigate this maze, but to be on the safe side, many Canadians wear a PFD in their boat, and carry lifejackets on board to meet the federal standard.

Inflatable PFDs

Lifejackets are designed for accidental immersion. They are intended to provide buoyancy and to maintain the body in a position that protects the airway. They are not designed to swim in, or for performing rescuers.

Still, lifejackets have gained popularity over the past several years due to their comfortable fit. While these PFDs certainly can be more comfortable, their need for a method of activation can be the device's Achilles heel. Some vests are equipped with a manual activator which requires conscious thought and effort to deploy. In the case of a head or spinal injury or a slow reaction time, this may not be possible. Conversely, some vests are equipped with an automatic activator which is initiated by water pressure. While removing the need for the wearer to deploy the vest, automatic inflation vests absolutely will inflate under pressure, including when the wearer is trapped in the fuselage or passenger area of a sinking helicopter or motor vehicle. This unwanted activation will trap the wearer inside the sinking equipment. They are therefore not recommended by the NFPA for rescuers.

1   US Coast Guard: http://www.uscg.mil/hq/cg5/cg5214 pfdselection.asp#commercialpfd

Helmets

The NFPA sets standards for helmets for surface water operations in the 1952 Standard. These helmets are designed to protect the head from impacts and must float. They must also be designed in such a manner that water will flow easily through them and not create a choking or injury hazard by "bucketing" or retaining water.

They must have a strong strap system and any metal parts must be corrosion resistant. The foam lining must not absorb so much water that it becomes heavy and uncomfortable to wear.

This standard does not address helmets to be worn in motorized or non-motorized boats.

Working at height helmets (EN 397) and mountaineering helmets (EN 12492) are designed to protect against objects falling from above. Most have a cradle that has a space between it and the top of the helmet. This space absorbs the energy from an impact. These helmets are not appropriate for use in swiftwater as the space can act as a bucket, catching the current, filling with water, and possibly leading to neck injuries. In extreme cases, the helmet could be ripped off, leaving the wearer unprotected.

Just because a helmet has holes does not mean it is meant for use in the water. Holes are usually intended for ventilation.

Footwear

Good footwear for the water rescue environment has always been a compromise. Recreational water shoes often have thin soles, making them unsuitable to work on rough river banks. Today there are a number of very good supportive boots available on the market and some even have climbing grade rubber soles. Water boots tend to take severe abuse from contaminated water, rough terrain, and long periods of being soaked followed by rapid drying.

Boots do not need to be waterproof (a drysuit with socks accomplishes this and so the wearer is protected from hazmat) but they must be non-slip on rough terrain, be flexible enough to swim in, and offer protection to the sole and toe area. Neoprene boots offer good insulation and will sustain constant drenching without rotting, unlike hiking boots. However, hiking boots may offer more grip and support on uneven terrain. Some industrial work boots are available. They are similar to hiking boots, but with additional steel or composite shank and toe-cap protection. The downside of using industrial boots is that they are heavy and do not drain well. This can be a distinct disadvantage in the water.

Gloves

Hands need protection in the water environment from cold, abrasion, and possibly hazmat. Neoprene gloves with reinforced palms offer warmth and some degree of protection from sharp objects. The NFPA specifies a cut-proof palm. However, if gloves are too thick, handling ropes becomes difficult and they do not offer any protection from hazmat. True dry gloves will provide hazmat protection but they become very cumbersome to swim in and for handling ropes etc. Make sure to choose your gloves carefully.

Whistle

A whistle that will continue to function after immersion in water is a vital tool for anyone operating at a water incident. Whistles can be used either to attract attention when in trouble, or as a communication system with specific calls. Swiftwater environments often have high levels of background noise created by moving water, and in many cases whistle blasts can be heard when vocal communication is not possible. They are also particularly useful during night operations.

Knives

Anyone working near the water environment with ropes must carry a knife. Ropes in water can become tangled and entrapped very easily. The knife carried needs to be very sharp and easily available, yet secure. Tying a knife on a lanyard to the PFD is not recommended, as this could become a hazard if open and thrashing around in the water when attached.

Throwbags

A throwbag is a standard water rescue tool and should be carried at all times when near water. It is comprised of a specialized water rescue rope contained in a bag for easy throwing.

Examples of throwbag types & sizes

Throwbags are available in various lengths depending upon their intended use, the most common being 50' (15m) to 75' (23m) long. The rope used is predominantly polypropylene; however, some specialist throwbags use ropes combining more than one material, such as nylon and spectra. All have a low melting point and therefore are unsuitable for high-angle rope rescue applications.

Must Float

The rope used in throwbags must float, as must the bag. Keeping the rope and bag on the surface of the water makes it easier for the victim to grab the rope and minimizes the chances of the rope tangling in debris.

Throwbags must be highly visible. The bags must be easy to pack and contain the rope easily and securely. Additional features such as lightstick holders, reflective tape and belt attachment points are all useful options.

Rope Diameter

Rope diameters vary and the thicker the rope, the easier it is to handle. Obviously, the thicker the rope is, the heavier it will be, and the larger the bag will be. Thicker rope also means that people with smaller hands may have difficulty throwing coils.

Commercially manufactured throwbags are available in a variety of lengths between 30' (9m) and 125' (38m). Smaller bags are easy to stow, carry, and throw but have limited range. Larger bags can be difficult to throw but are invaluable on wider channels. Remember, you can always make a long rope easier to throw by removing a few feet of rope from the bag before throwing, but it is much harder to make a short rope longer.

Lights

When personnel are working at night they need adequate lighting. This may be provided by portable generators and flood lighting, or from vehicles.

Personnel in the field need personal lighting. Headlamps are ideal, as they give a hands-free capability and light up wherever the individual looks. Headlamps are good for lighting the immediate personal space. LED bulb technology now delivers a pure white light and an extended battery life. Backup lights and batteries should be carried.

For search operations, headlamps are generally not powerful enough and do not cast light a sufficient distance. For this task, powerful handheld spotlights are required.

For rescuers who will operate in the water, the headlamps and lights need to be waterproof.

Emergency lights for personnel, such as Cyalume glow sticks, are advisable. Although they do not provide working light, they are very effective for locating equipment, or personnel if their personal lights fail.

4

Swim Fins

Swim fins can greatly increase a rescuer's speed when swimming in water. However, they can be difficult and tiring to use in swiftwater and are awkward when moving about on shore. Normal diving fins are too large for use in swiftwater, but specialist river fins are available from a number of manufacturers

Eye Protection

Water can act like snow in reflecting and magnifying light, and so if prolonged time is expected on the water in sunny conditions, suitable sunglasses that block 99-100% of UVA and UVB light can be used to help protect the eyes from damage. While polarization does not afford any further protection, it does cut glare from horizontal surfaces, such as water, and gives clearer, crisper vision.

If wearing eye protection, the benefits of cutting glare should be considered alongside possibility of impact, and operational issues, such as fogging. If an additional risk to rescuers' eyes is present (such as using hydraulic cutting tools on a vehicle in the water) then suitable eye protection should be worn.

Buoyant Aids

Although relatively rare in swiftwater rescue, for many years lifeguards have used buoyant aids to reduce the risk posed by the victim. Many different designs are available. They all work on the same basic principle of providing a large amount of buoyancy in an easy-to-grip shape and a length of rope that allows rescuers to distance themselves from the victim.

Technical and team equipment

Rescue teams carry a vast range of equipment, depending on their areas and levels of operation. Awareness level personnel are not rescue team members but do need to have knowledge of the equipment used as they may perform a supporting role in the cold zone (see page 172).

Proper use of the correct technical equipment is an integral part of many water rescue situations. By using a small amount of equipment and some basic techniques, a rescuer will be able to set up systems which may make a rescue much safer and more efficient.

Ropes

Ropes are used for a variety of applications in water rescue. It is essential that the correct type of rope is used for each application. The characteristics and properties of a rope will depend upon the methods of construction and the materials used in its construction.

Ropes and knots

As a rule of thumb, the tensile strength of a rope will decrease by approximately 30% when a knot is tied into it. This is because not all the fibers in the rope are equally loaded, and indeed some are redundant due to the turns and loops tied.

Rope construction

Some common materials used in modern rope construction and their properties include:

Nylon

- High tensile strength
- High elasticity
- High energy absorption
- High impact resistance
- It will soften at 230°C (446°F)
- It does not float and can absorb water, which reduces its strength

Polyester

- High tensile strength
- Low elasticity
- High melting point (249°C/480.2°F)
- Good abrasion resistance
- No reduction in strength when wet
- Does not float

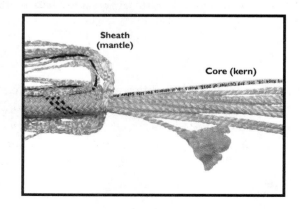

Polypropylene

- Strength is approximately 50% of nylon or polyester of the same thickness
- It will soften at 165°C (329°F)
- Floats in water
- Minimal strength reduction when wet
- Polypropylene is not as abrasion resistant as polyethylene

Polyethylene

- About 5% less strength than polypropylene
- About 5% heavier than polypropylene
- Low melting point (138°C/280.4°F)
- Often used in non-critical applications where buoyancy is required, e.g., water skiing tow ropes

Aramids, e.g., Kevlar

- Resistant to high temperatures
- Very high tensile strength
- Very low stretch (1.5-3% stretch at failure)
- Poor shock absorbing ability
- Does not float
- Increasingly used in winching operations

HMPE (high modulus polyethylene), e.g., Spectra, Dyneema

- Very strong
- Very low stretch (2.7-3.5% stretch at failure)
- Poor shock absorbing properties
- Low melting point (135°C/275°F)
- Floats and no reduction in strength when wet
- Very slippery and does not hold knots well

Most modern ropes for water and rope rescue are kernmantle in construction. This German word means core (kern) and sheath (mantle).

The central core of fibers provides the majority of the rope's strength, and these are protected by a woven sheath. The sheath provides a lesser portion of the strength, but also protects the core from abrasion, dirt and UV damage. This construction method produces ropes which are strong, resistant to damage, and easy to handle. Some ropes found in throwbags can be of a braided construction, as opposed to kernmantle construction.

Floating ropes – types and usage

For water rescue, a rope that floats is essential. They are easier to work with, and greatly reduce the possibility of entanglements with in-water objects.

Throwbag rope

Most throwbag ropes are constructed from polypropylene in a bright color. This provides a high visibility rope that is soft to handle (packs well into the throwbag) and floats well. They are not designed for use in hauling or high tension applications. Due to the low melting point, they should only be used in conjunction with rope grabs and Prusik knots with extreme caution.

Combination water rescue ropes

4

A number of specialist water rescue ropes are now available, which mix construction materials to create specialist properties for water rescue work. These include:

Nylon sheath/polypropylene core

Sheath provides abrasion resistance and core provides flotation.

Polypropylene sheath/HMPE core

Core material provides extra strength.

Water rescue ropes are now available that glow in the dark for low light rescue work.

These water rescue ropes are designed for in-water use and not for high angle work and rescue applications.

Canyoning ropes

A number of specialist ropes are now available for use in the sport of canyoning, and as such are designed for lowering and abseiling in canyons. The majority of these are floating ropes, but not all are – so check the manufacturer's information. Many canyoning ropes will be semi-static ropes. When rated for it these are excellent for in-water applications that involve higher loads and the use of mechanical advantage systems, e.g., rescues from vehicles in water.

Non-floating ropes – types and usage

These will almost exclusively be made from nylon. Depending upon use, they will either be classified as dynamic or semi–static ropes.

It is not possible to tell from inspection whether a rope is a dynamic, semi-static, or indeed a specialist water rescue rope, as they can look and feel the same and be the same color. Proper recording, marking and logging of rope is required to avoid potentially lethal confusion.

Dynamic ropes (High stretch)

These ropes are designed to stretch in order to cope with the dynamic loads created by falling rock climbers and mountaineers. They are of limited use in water rescue applications.

Static ropes (Low stretch)

These are low stretch ropes, commonly used for rope access and rope rescue applications. Generally, they are 11mm (7/16") - 12.5mm (1/2") in diameter. Their strength and relatively low stretch characteristics make them ideal for high load applications, such as the track line for boat on a highline rescue systems and any high angle rescue applications. The NFPA 1983 standard identifies two types of rope – type A and type B. The main difference is that type A ropes are defined as heavy duty. Type B ropes are weaker and designated as light duty. Only type A ropes should be used as the main and safety lines in high angle rescue situations.

Accessory cord

Non-floating low stretch rope is available in a variety of smaller diameters, for use as accessory cords and applications such as making Prusik loops. Prusik loops are generally either made from 6mm or 8mm cord.

Webbing

Most webbing is made from nylon or polyester, and is available in tubular or flat. Due to its characteristics, it may be preferred over rope in certain applications. It is cheaper than rope, and due to its wide, flat surface, it is less susceptible to abrasion[2]. There are fewer secure knots for use in webbing (normally a water knot is used). As a result, it is common to use pre-sewn webbing slings.

---

2   www.hse.gov.uk/research/crr_pdf/2001/crr01364.pdf

Use of rope protection

Ropes and webbing are highly susceptible to damage when rubbing on edges and rough objects, especially when under tension. Wherever ropes are at risk of damage, they should be protected. A variety of specially designed protectors are used, plus more general material such as canvas. Testing has suggested that some of the best rope protection performance was achieved with canvas, which was also one of the cheapest.

Care of ropes, storage and recording

Ropes should be dried after use and then stored in a cool, dry location away from light. If needed, ropes can be washed according to the manufacturer's recommendations. The life of a rope will be determined by how well it is cared for and the use it has had. Rope usage needs to be logged and each rope should have its own identification code, marking and rope log.

The general rule is that ropes should be used for up to a maximum of five years once issued (unless condition or usage dictates an earlier retirement). Additionally, the rope can be stored for up to five years before being issued. This means that if a rope is purchased and stored but never issued and used, it should still be retired and destroyed after ten years.

Rope log		
Rope ID:		
Diameter:		
Length:		
Make:		
Model:		
Color:		
Purchased from:		
Purchase date:		
Date in service:		
Batch number:		
Serial number:		
Date	Use / inspection	Name

Example of rope log sheet

Technical hardware

Carabiners

These are metal connectors that are used to clip together ropes, slings, webbing, etc. Carabiners come in many shapes and sizes. They are made from steel or aluminum alloy.

Steel has the advantage of being stronger and cheaper than similar aluminum alloy, but has the disadvantage of being heavier and prone to rust.

Aluminum alloy carabiners have an excellent strength to weight ratio and are generally used for water rescue applications. Although they do not rust, they are susceptible to corrosion, especially if exposed to sea water.

Carabiners (from left) - pear-shaped bent snapgate, oval screwgate, D-shaped screwgate, Pear-shaped screwgate

Carabiners are available as either snapgate or locking gate designs. As the name suggests, locking gate carabiners have a locking mechanism on the opening gate. This makes them safer for use in safety-critical applications, such as clipping a rope to a quick-release chest harness.

There are a number of designs for this locking mechanism, ranging from traditional screwgates through to more modern twist lock designs. Screw gates require the user to manually lock the gate closed, whereas twist lock systems will automatically do so.

It is important that carabiners are used correctly, to ensure they are used to their full strength. The load should be applied along the major axis with the gate locked. This ensures the carabiner maintains its full strength.

Descent Control

These devices are used to control the rope under load, often referred to as belay devices or friction devices. There are many variations available.

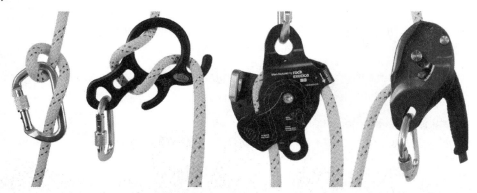

Belay devices (from left) - Italian hitch (Münter hitch), Figure Eight Descender, MPD, Petzl I'D

Whichever method is used to control a rope, it is essential the manufacturer's instructions are followed.

In water rescue, these devices can be used in a number of situations, including tensioning lines and controlling the movement of boats.

Rope grabs

A rope grab is a device which locks onto the rope, to grip against a pulling force from one or both directions.

This may be a mechanical device, or a non-mechanical device, such as a Prusik knot.

Some rope grabs have a toothed design. These are generally designed for use of a single person load only. If they are overloaded, they can cause critical rope damage.

Rope grabs (from left) - Petzl Rescucender, Petzl handled ascender, triple wrap Prusik, klemheist Prusik

Pulleys

A pulley is a wheeled device which is used to reduce friction when the rope changes direction. There are a wide variety of designs and shapes for use in particular applications, such as Prusik-minding, knot-passing and tandem pulleys.

Examples of various types of pulleys

Inflated fire hose

Capping and inflating a fire hose with compressed air gives a number of water rescue options. The hose can be used as a reach rescue tool in flat or slow moving water. It is also useful in lowhead dams, where the hose is pushed into the towback to reach the victim. It can be used as a pendulum rescue lowered from a bridge or as a downstream backup when set up as a diagonal. See page 126.

The kit is comprised of: lengths of standard fire hose, cylinder(s) of compressed air, caps for the hose ends, and an inflation/deflation control system. The first stage regulates the flow pressure from the cylinder then a further reducer on the inflation system regulates the flow into the hose. The hose for most applications is inflated between one and three bar.

Using a hose to perform a reach rescue

Boats

Boats come in many shapes and sizes and have a multitude of uses. No boat exists which fulfills all the needs of the water and flood rescuer. Compromises are necessary, and it is critical for rescuers to understand their craft's capabilities and limitations. For more information on the use of boats, see section 6.

Flood events can be divided into phases (see page 42). Different flood phases will require different types of response. For example, evacuation, rescue, search and rescue, search and recovery. The high speed water conditions associated with phase two of a flood event may require a fast, powerful craft to deal with water velocity. Phases three and four of a flood event may require a more robust, puncture-proof and simple response. Each craft has advantages and disadvantages.

Think carefully about the end use of the boat, not the romantic image portrayed in the catalogue. The sheer number and variety of boats currently on the market is huge and can be confusing. Some questions which should be asked of your team before purchasing a boat should be:

- What will the boat be used for?
- How will it be transported?
- On what type of water will it be used?
- Where can it be launched?
- How many crew are needed to operate it safely?

Inflatable rescue boat (IRB)

These tend to be smaller boats with a raft like construction. They can be rolled up for transportation and launched very easily. They have a rigid transom on which to attach an engine, and can have a semi-rigid floor, e.g., a number of aluminum strips covered with Hypalon. They sometimes have an inflatable keel which improves directional control and helps in rougher water. IRBs tend to be forgiving and maneuverable in whitewater and can also be handled reasonably efficiently without the motor. They are also compartmentalized like whitewater rafts.

This type of boat is proving to be very popular with a lot of emergency services and rescue teams, due to its versatility and friendly handling characteristics, along with its ease of carrying to and launching at rescue sites. Its ability to carry loads or people is not as great as other boats, and it can become very unstable if overloaded. As it is lightweight, it can easily be waded in shallow water.

Rigid hull craft

Rigid hulled boats come in a huge variety of shapes and sizes - they can have flat bottoms or deep Vs. They can be made of a wide variety of durable materials, such as aluminum, wood or plastic. Some boats have a double skin or built-in buoyancy compartments which keep the boat afloat if it swamps. Those that have a flat bottom tend to have good initial stability, though they will feel more unstable in rough water. The deeper V a boat has, the less initial stability it will have, but it will handle rougher weather and waves better.

Rigid hulled boats also tend to have more freeboard - that is, higher sides. This can cause problems when recovering victims in to the boat. Almost all will need a trailer and slipway to launch. This type of boat is easily available and can be very versatile as long as the limitations of its particular design are respected.

Rigid inflatable boat (RIB)

These have a combination of a rigid hull and keel with inflatable tubes much like that of a raft. The larger size of a RIB (compared to the IRB) allows it to use much more powerful engines. This is a great combination of the rigid hull for speed and directional stability, with the forgiving nature and stability of the inflated side tubes. Larger RIBs can have a central console with a wheel and throttle control, which gives a better view of the water and victim, though you do lose a certain directness of steering response obtainable from a tiller-steered boat.

As with other rigid hulled craft, it usually needs to be launched from a trailer.

Personal water craft (PWC)

PWCs do suffer from a bad image of being the hooligan's tool of choice. This statement has to be revised due to the increased use of the PWC in water-based rescues. The PWC has long been used in surf rescue, where its power, speed, and maneuverability have earned it quite a reputation as a formidable rescue craft. Due to the jet drive, there is no prop to foul or injure victims in the water. However, if the jet intake gets clogged, they lose power instantly.

This craft is still in its infancy for river or moving water rescue, though its potential is considerable. PWCs require trailer launching.

Whitewater raft

These range in size from around 3.5m to 5m And are usually made of a rubberized material called Hypalon. They can also be made from PVC, which is lighter but not as tough or abrasion resistant. Whitewater rafts are easily carried and launched almost anywhere. Due to their lightness, they are easily waded around in shallow water.

Whitewater rafts are almost always paddle-powered and obviously rely on a high skill level from the crew. Most rafts now come with inflatable floors with simple drain holes to create a very effective drainage system. This allows the raft to run difficult water without worrying about bailing out water. The tubes of the raft are also compartmentalized to prevent a puncture in one tube deflating the whole boat.

Rafts provide a very stable platform for numerous other rescue scenarios and so can be a huge asset to the rescue team. They can be used successfully in lowhead dam rescue, on a high line, and for quick access to submerged vehicles, either free paddled or on a tensioned diagonal rope system.

Types of propulsion

When choosing the boat, the method of propulsion needs to be decided at the same time. There is a choice of paddle power or engine power to propel the chosen boat. Which is appropriate will depend very much on the situation or rescue at hand. The Swiftwater and Flood Rescue Technician (SRT) syllabus contains an optional session on paddleboat handling, which can be extended by taking the Swiftwater Paddle Boat Handling (SPBH) course. For training in motor powered boats, Rescue 3 offers a Swiftwater and Flood Rescue Boat Operator (SFRBO) course.

Whatever type of craft is chosen, it is essential to be aware of its limitations when it is paddle powered as opposed to motor powered. A large RIB, for instance, is extremely difficult to paddle, due to the deep V hull making directional changes difficult. The distance from the water that the paddler will sit, especially near the bow, also creates difficulties. However, a small IRB or whitewater raft is easily paddled and maneuvered, and indeed even waded.

All paddle-powered boats can basically only move downstream. While it is possible to break out and even move upstream in eddies, they are at the mercy of the direction of flow. For a crew to be able to paddle a boat efficiently in flowing water, they must have trained and practiced together on a regular basis. The deployment speed of a paddle boat can be a huge advantage in a rescue scenario.

Other craft

Kayak

- Extremely maneuverable
- High skill level required
- Very limited carrying capacity
- Paddled
- Robust
- Very specialized craft with limited app

Canoe

- Maneuverable
- High skill level required
- Limited carrying capacity
- Paddled or waded
- Robust
- Versatile but specialized

Inflatable rescue platforms (pathways)

- Not a boat
- Designed for unstable surfaces such as mud and ice
- Spread load across wide area for support on unstable surface
- Unsuitable for flowing water and evacuating flood victims

Rescue boards and sleds

- Useful to support a swimming rescue
- Quick to set up
- Requires an in-water option - victim exposed to the water
- Variety of designs available for mud and ice work, surf rescue, flood rescue, and to be used in conjunction with a PWC

4

Knots and anchor systems

In order to carry out many of the tasks associated with rescue from water, it is essential that a technician is suitably skilled and experienced in the following areas:

- Tying knots and hitches
- Building anchors and anchor systems
- Belaying
- Creating mechanical advantage systems

Rope terminology

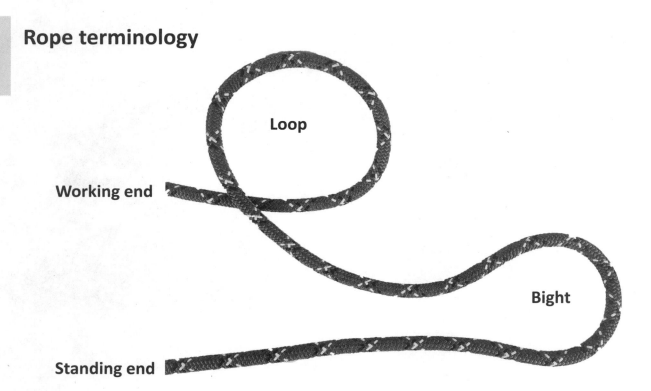

Parts of a rope

Knots and hitches

There are a multitude of knots and hitches, but only a small number of them are required by a rescue technician. These knots and hitches need to become second nature so that they can be tied reliably and quickly when needed, including at night and underwater.

If sufficient length of tail is left, then knots should not require the tying of additional stopper knots. A general rule of thumb is 15cm (6") of tail.

Once a knot is tied in a rope, it will reduce the strength of the rope. This is due to the rope going through a sharp turn. The fibers on the outside of the turn will end up taking the majority of the load, while the fibers on the inside of the turn don't take as much. The exact amount of strength loss will depend on how tight the turns are in the knot, and will vary from individual knot to individual knot. Knots should be dressed so that they look well-tied and load evenly. This will help maximize the strength of the knot.

As a general rule of thumb, deduct a third of the tensile strength of a rope once it has a knot tied in it.

4

A thorough investigation into the relative strengths of knots was undertaken in the UK by Lyon Equipment on behalf of the Health and Safety Executive. A copy of the full report is available at www.hse.gov.uk/research/crr_pdf/2001/crr01364.pdf. A similar and thorough study was also conducted by CMC Rescue in 2014.[3]

After use, knots should be removed from the rope before the rope is returned to storage. Knots left in the rope for extended periods tend to set and become difficult to untie. If a knot is untied after having been in place for a long time, the rope where the knot was will be weaker than before the knot was in place.

The website www.animatedknots.com is an excellent resource with step by step photos of how to tie most common knots.

Overhand knot

This simple to tie knot is commonly used as a stopper knot on the end of a rope.

Overhand on a bight

By doubling over the end of the rope to form a bight, an overhand knot is tied to create a loop. This is easy to tie but can be difficult to untie once loaded.

Figure of eight knot

Similar to an overhand knot but with one extra turn. The figure of eight shape is easily recognizable. This is commonly used as a stopper knot on the end of a rope.

3 McKently, John. CMC Rescue. Rescue Knot Efficiency Revisited. Presented at the International Technical Rescue Symposium, 2014.

Figure of eight on a bight

By doubling over the end of the rope to form a bight, a figure of eight knot is tied to create a loop in the end of rope. It is important that this knot is only loaded in one direction.

Re-threaded figure of eight (figure of eight follow through)

This knot allows a loop to be made at the end of a rope around an object such as a tree or post, when a figure of eight on a bight cannot be tied. It is commonly used in anchor applications. Begin by tying a figure of eight (see previous), then take the end of the rope around the object, before re-threading it through the initial figure of eight knot.

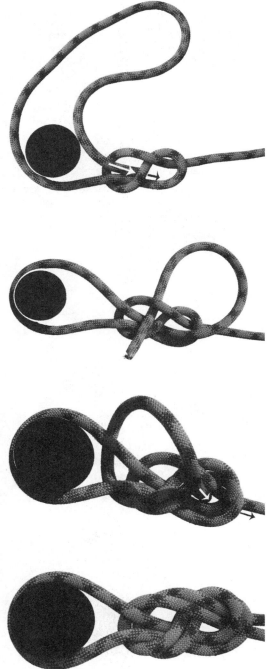

Alpine butterfly

This knot creates a loop in the middle of a rope that can be loaded in multiple directions. It can also be used to isolate a damaged section of rope.

Begin by wrapping the rope around the hand, so that there are three strands in the palm.

Take the strand nearest the thumb, and move it to the fingertips, lifting it over the top of the other two strands.

Take the new strand that is nearest the thumb, and move it to the fingertips, lifting it over the top of the other two strands.

Slide the thumb underneath the strands and take hold of the furthest strand (the one that has just been placed there). Pull the hand out.

Remove the hand completely. To dress the knot correctly, pull the ends of the rope apart.

The alpine butterfly correctly dressed. This is the reverse side of the knot shown in the above picture.

Water knot (overhand bend, ring bend, tape knot)

This is used for tying together two pieces of similar webbing or joining two ends of the same piece to make a loop. It is important that this knot is dressed properly to maximize its strength.

The water knot starts with a simple overhand knot (see above). Ensure that the webbing sits flat and is not twisted or kinked.

Starting from the working end of the first webbing (dark), feed the end of the second webbing (light) into the overhand knot.

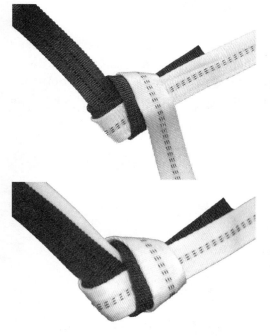

Feed the webbing all the way through the overhand knot.

4

The completed knot, tied loosely to show the construction.

The water knot loaded. Once the water knot has been fully loaded, it can be impossible to untie.

Clove hitch

This can be used to secure the middle of a rope around objects such as carabiners or fire hoses. As they are prone to slippage, they should not be used on the end of a rope.

Italian hitch (Münter hitch)

This is a movable hitch that is normally tied around specially shaped carabiners (HMS or pear-shaped). The hitch creates friction as it moves over the carabiners and itself. It can be used for controlling the movement of loads. It will reverse automatically so rope can be let out or taken in.

Tying off an Italian hitch

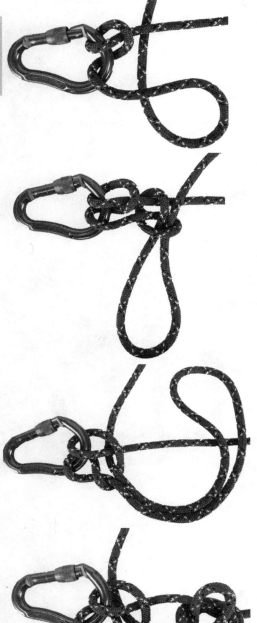

Form a loop in the rope.

Push a bight of rope through the loop.

Pull enough of the bight of rope through to tie an overhand knot around the tensioned part of the rope.

The tied off Italian hitch.

Double fisherman's bend

This is used for joining the ends of two similar sized ropes. It can be very difficult to untie once loaded. Commonly, this is used with accessory cord (6-8mm) to make Prusik loops (see Prusik loops on next page). This knot is often used to make prusik loops.

For clarity, ropes of two different colors have been used. Start with the two ends of the rope overlapping.

Loop one of the ropes around the other.

Continue to loop the rope around – travelling back on itself. A cross should have formed.

Feed the working end of the rope underneath the cross to form the first double fisherman's knot.

When correctly tied and dressed, the knot should form a neat cross shape on one side.

Repeat the process with the other rope. Note that this rope is wrapping around in the opposite direction.

Continue to wrap the rope around until another cross is formed.

Feed the working end of the rope underneath the cross. At this stage, ensure that the two crosses formed by the two knots are on the same side. This is a common error - if the crosses are not next to each other, it is necessary to untie one of the knots and re-tie it in the opposite direction.

Both double fisherman's knots tied correctly.

The double fisherman's bend, tightened and dressed. Note the compact and neat appearance of the knot.

Prusik loops

Originally developed by mountaineers for ascending fixed ropes, these loops of cordage are very useful – particularly in constructing mechanical advantage systems. Prusik loops are presewn by companies like Sterling, or they are created by making a loop of 6-8mm cord or tape and wrapping this around the main rope, usually with the fisherman's knot. A new cordage called hollowblock is becoming more and more popular due to its abililty to grip on any diameter rope. When loaded, these hitches grip the main rope, but when unloaded can be slid along the main rope and repositioned. There are a large number of hitches that can accomplish this with different properties and applications. Two of the most common for water rescue applications are:

Triple wrap Prusik

This is tied using cord that is approximately half the diameter of the main rope, for example an 11mm rope would require a 6-8mm Prusik loop. It cannot be released under normal working loads. However, it will demonstrate a tendency to slip given an excessive load.

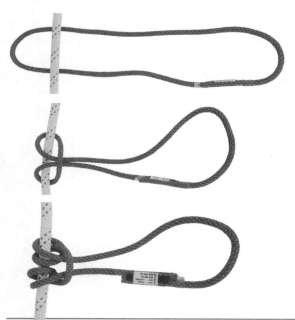

When starting the Prusik knot, ensure that the double fisherman's bend is slightly to one side. Otherwise the knot can end up inside the Prusik knot.

Wrap the Prusik loop around the main rope and feed it back through itself, to form a loose lark's foot.

Wrap the Prusik loop around the main rope again, and feed it back through the loop again.

Wrap the Prusik loop around the main rope for a third time to complete the triple wrap Prusik.

The triple wrap Prusik in action. Notice that the pull is from the center of the knot.

4

Klemheist

If a loop of webbing is being used, then the klemheist is the best Prusik knot to use. As with a triple wrap Prusik it cannot be released under normal working loads but will slip if excessive loads are applied.

Start with the end of the webbing loop a few inches clear of the main rope.

Wrap the webbing around the rope at least four times.

Feed the remainder of the webbing loop up through the end of the loop. The direction of pull is from left to right.

Anchoring

The ability to select reliable anchor points and construct anchor systems is a key skill for the Rescue Technician.

Good anchor selection is a result of experience and judgment gained over time. Bombproof anchor points, such as large boulders and trees, may be sufficient as single anchor points, even for some of the largest forces we will find in water rescue situations (e.g., anchoring submerged vehicles). However, these are often not available and we may need to use more than one anchor point and construct an anchor system so that the load is shared between more than one anchor – multiple point anchors.

Single point anchors

No-knot (full strength tie-off)

This is one of the simplest anchor systems to construct, but also one of the most versatile. The rope is wrapped around a suitable object (tree, post etc) and surface friction secures the rope in place. The surface friction of the object will determine how many times the rope needs to be wrapped around the object.

Wrap in an upwards direction. This stops the rope unwrapping.

Keep your wraps tight and tidy.

As there is no actual knot tied in the rope, the rope does not have its strength reduced. It is also a clean line (see "The clean rope principle" on page 118.

If you wish, the unloaded end of the rope can be clipped onto the loaded line with a carabiner for added security. However, the line will no longer be clean.

Basket hitch

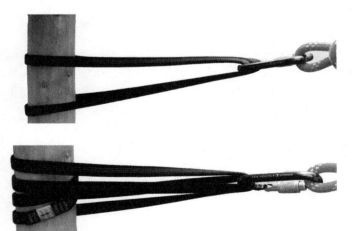

This is a sewn sling or knotted sling to either wrap around an object or thread between two objects. Both ends of the tape are then clipped together to complete the anchor. Sewn slings work best here, as any knot tied in tape will see the full load applied to it, and consequently can be difficult to untie.

A wrapped basket hitch. The extra wrap means that the hitch grips the post better, and is less likely to slide down it.

Single point with follow through knot

A similar anchor can be constructed by tying a re-threaded figure of eight knot around the anchor point. This can be used where a full strength tie-off would not be suitable. It does not need a tape sling and carabiners, but can result in the figure of eight knot being difficult to untie.

Wrap three, pull two

This is a very versatile and useful anchor. It is constructed by wrapping a length of tape around the anchor three times and joining the ends with a tape knot. Two of the wraps are then pulled to isolate the knot on the third wrap, which cinches onto the anchor object. The two other wraps are connected to the rope system with a carabiner.

The advantages of this system are:

- The knot is isolated from the full load and thus remains easy to untie after use.
- The anchor point is made of multiple wraps of tape and thus has increased strength – always assuming the object they are wrapped around is of sufficient size and strength.

Multi-point anchor systems

The forces involved in water rescue can be applied in many directions, due to the constantly moving water. In rope rescue, the forces are created by gravity in one fixed direction.

Depending upon how multi-point anchor systems are constructed, they can be made so that they will work in a range of directions should the loading direction move (load-distributing anchor) or only work in one set direction (load-sharing anchor).

Load-distributing anchors

- Distribute the load to multiple anchors as the load direction changes.
- Should one anchor fail in the system, the others will be shock-loaded.
- Ideal for use in water-based applications, where the direction of loading may change, e.g., recovering a pinned boat.

4

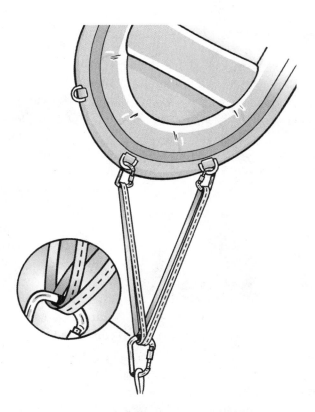

Two-point load-distributing anchor with a sling

When anchoring to the D-rings on an inflatable craft, it is essential that a multi-point anchor is used, due to the D-rings only being welded or glued on. By using a multi-point anchor, this will spread the load across several D-rings. It also ensure if one fails, there is a backup.
One of the easiest systems to use for this is the boatman's knot.

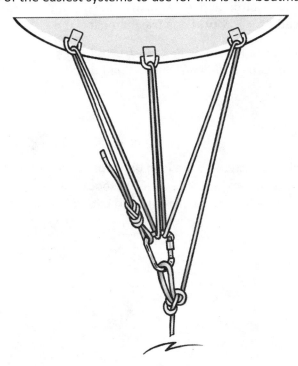

Three point boatman's

Load-sharing anchors

- Set up to work in one direction only
- Should one anchor fail, the others will not be shock-loaded
- Should the direction of loading move, the full load will come onto only one anchor point, with the others receiving no load
- Generally used out of water, where the direction of load is set by the action of gravity, e.g., vertical/ high angle rescue solutions

Anchors

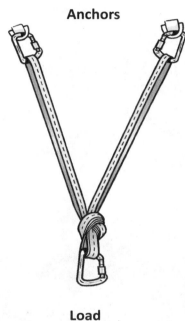

Load

Internal angles

Whenever a load is shared between two or more anchor points, the actual amount of loading each anchor receives is dependent upon the internal angle created at the focus point.

If the load is shared between two anchor points next to each other, so that both legs of the anchor system are essentially parallel, then each anchor point will receive half the force of the load.

As the anchor points move apart, then the internal angle will be increased, and each anchor point will see an increased loading.

At an internal angle of 90°, each anchor will see a force of approximately 70% of the load.

At an internal angle of 120°, each anchor point will see a force equal to the full load.

As the internal angle increases above 120°, the loading on each anchor point will be increasingly larger than the load being supported. For example, at 160° each anchor will receive a force equal to three times the load.

As we want to reduce the loading on each anchor point in the system, we need to keep the internal angle as small as possible, and certainly 90° or less. We can also use our outstretched hand to create a useful 90° set square.

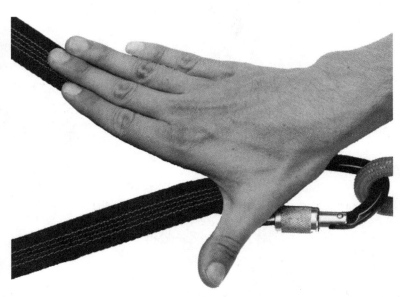

Using a hand to measure the internal angle of an anchor system

Tensioning systems and mechanical advantage

Mechanical advantage (MA) can assist the rescuer to move a heavy load or oppose a large force. Commonly, rescuers will use mechanical advantage to either tension ropes, stabilize objects or haul loads.

Energy cannot be created, so mechanical advantage works on the principle that a large load can be moved over a short distance by a smaller load moving over a longer distance.

In order to lift a 3kN load (about 775 lb force) up 3 feet (1m), a 3:1 MA system can be built. The load will then move by applying a 1kN (225 lb) force to it. However, the cost is that 9 ft (3m) of rope will need to be pulled through the MA system to move the load 3 ft (1m).

Mechanical advantage can be achieved through a number of methods, e.g., levers. In water and rope rescue, mechanical advantage is usually created by the use of pulleys and rope.

Depending upon the arrangement of pulleys, a vast range of mechanical advantage systems can be created. These can be divided into three categories:

4

- Simple mechanical advantage systems
- Compound mechanical advantage systems
- Complex mechanical advantage systems

Rescue Technicians need to know a few easy to remember methods of creating mechanical advantage. If these do not work, it is often because the pull is in the wrong direction, as opposed to not using enough MA.

The flowing water should be read and, whenever possible, use it to help rather than hinder operations. The ideal angle of pull needs to be identified before rigging any systems.

The Six Rules of Mechanical Advantage

1. If the attachment point originates at the anchor the MA will be EVEN.

2. If the attachment point originates at the load the MA will be ODD.

3. Pulleys or bends that move with the load create Mechanical Advantage.

4. Stationary pulleys are a change of direction.

5. When you add pulleys in a simple MA you add the Mechanical Advantage.

6. When you stack pullies/MA's in a compound MA you multiply the Mechanical Advantage.

Basic MA systems

Strong arm method

Not a true MA system, since the force is increased by adding more people into the system to haul. However, it can often be the simplest, quickest and most efficient solution – assuming the manpower is available.

Load

Vector pull

Once a line is tensioned and secured, a force can be applied at right angles to the line to create a mechanical advantage. Once the vector force is applied, it will have the effect of reducing the angle on the main line which is operating as a force multiplier. Consequently, the effectiveness of the vector pull in creating mechanical advantage is quickly diminished.

3:1 simple MA system

This easy to rig system is the most common basic mechanical advantage system.

This system can be rigged either on the rope itself (internal MA) or using a separate rope attached onto the haul rope (external MA).

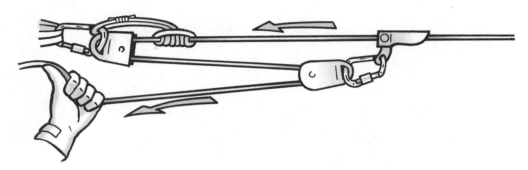

Simple 3:1 mechanical advantage (internal)

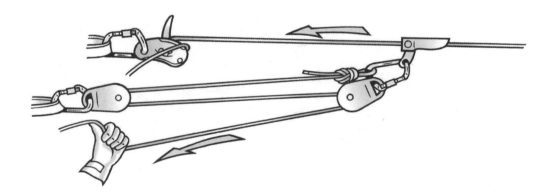

Simple 3:1 mechanical advantage (external or piggy back)

5:1 simple MA system

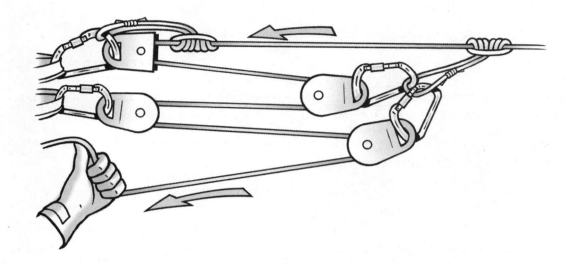

9:1 compound MA system

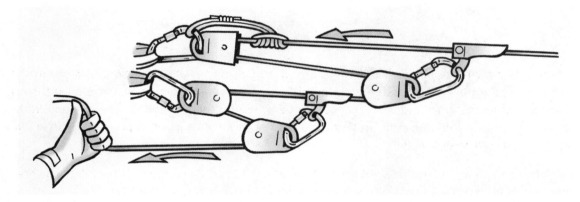

These diagrams are expanded for clarity. Ideally, the haul rope will be as close to the load ropes as possible.

T method – calculating mechanical advantage

Working out how much mechanical advantage a system creates can be difficult to learn. T method is one of the easiest and most practical ways of doing this, which works regardless of whether the system is simple, compound or complex.

The underpinning principal of this method is that everything must balance.

Always start calculating mechanical advantage from the haul team. The haul team always pull with the force of one unit. The rope then travels through a pulley with a load of one unit. Then there is one unit in the rope going into the pulley and also one unit in the rope leaving the pulley. These units must then be balanced with two units on the other side of the pulley, and anything else attached to it, for example a carabiner.

If this principal is applied to the system in the diagram below and assume a nominal force of one unit from the hauler, it can be followed through the system.

3:1 system explained using T method.

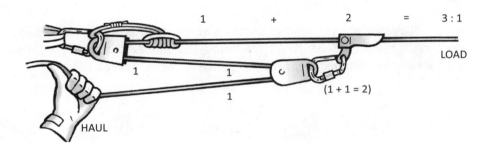

This force of one unit from the hauler is in the rope as it enters the traveling pulley. It remains in the rope as it leaves the traveling pulley. This creates a force of two units in the pulley, which is carried through the carabiners and into the rope grab. The one unit in the rope continues through the ID. The one unit in the rope is added to the two units in the rope grab which gives a total of three units being applied to the load. Thus the mechanical advantage of the system is 3:1.

T method can be used to calculate the **ideal** mechanical advantage of any system. No mechanical advantage system ever works that well. T method does not account for external factors such as:

- Frictional loss
- Heat loss
- Rope stretch
- Slippage, and many other things

In-water victim management

For effective victim management in the water, the person must be brought to the bank or an eddy. From that stable position, the patient can be packaged onto a back board or into a litter.

Complications arise where a spinal injury is suspected. If the victim is face down in the water, it is imperative they are rolled over onto their backs as a matter of urgency. Airway always takes priority over spinal injuries. There are several techniques to roll over a patient and maintain spinal alignment.

Studies[4] suggest that spinal injuries are not an emergency that occurs very often in an aquatic environment (including swimming pools and beaches). However, there are no significant clinical studies on spinal cord injury management techniques in an aquatic setting. It is not possible to recommend one technique over any other. There are only anecdotal reports and opinions. Treatment of spinal cord injury is primarily focused on doing no more harm.

Buoyancy Aid technique

If the victim is wearing a buoyancy aid, the rescuer should carefully approach them, and cross his arms. Both thumbs should be pointing at the floor. The victim's head should be squeezed between the rescuer's forearms. Gripping the buoyancy aid shoulder straps, the rescuer untwists his arms, turning the victim face-up.

 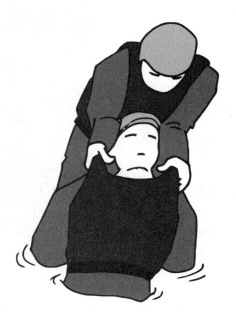

Buoyancy aid technique

---

4   Watson RS, Cummings P, Quan L, et al. (2001) Cervical spine injuries among submersion victims. J Trauma 51:658–662

Extended arm grip

The extended arm grip is the name given by the International Lifesaving Federation (ILSF) to a technique that is also sometimes known as the head splint.

The rescuer approaches the victim, and gently raises their arms up to either side of the head of the victim. The arms are then squeezed against the victim's head to provide cervical spine stabilization. The rescuer places their thumbs on the back of the victim's head to prevent it from slipping backwards. If necessary, the victim can be rolled face-up.

Place the hands on their arms, squeezing the victim's arms against their head.

Gently roll the victim onto their back, squeeze them into your chest, maintaining a secure grip on their arms.
Remain low in the water to avoid lifting the victim.

Once the victim is rolled onto their back using the appropriate technique, the head and neck should be continually supported. The victim should then be fitted with a neck collar and transferred to a longboard with head blocks in a safe area of water.

Where a victim is to be transported across an area of water, they must not be secured to the board, as this would result in the victim being held upside down underwater should the board be lost downstream.

Medical and decontamination considerations

Falling in

Personnel falling into the water is a foreseeable hazard of working near water. All team members should be aware of the danger and prepared for this. All personnel who work within the warm zone must be dressed in suitable PPE which will provide protection if they fall in. Personnel should be aware of the area they are working in and understand the water characteristics should they become immersed.

Defensive swimming

Upon immersion, a lifejacket is designed to float the wearer on their back with the face clear of the water. Personnel should adopt the defensive swimming position. This will help protect them from underwater obstructions, allow them to make small adjustments to their position in the water and assist with looking where they are going.

The person in the water needs assistance from other team members to get back to the bank and out of the water.

Personal welfare

Welfare is an important issue when personnel are committed to rescue scenes.

Working in harsh environments quickly takes its toll on stamina. Personnel will require regular breaks, rotation of teams, feeding, re-hydration, warming and/or cooling. It is essential that team leaders and managers recognize this and make provision for the welfare of the team members, and also the members of the public and casualties involved in an incident.

At major flood events many teams will be required to allow for adequate rotation and resting of teams. Accommodation will be required so personnel can rest, sleep and recuperate away from the scene. Consideration must be given to cleaning equipment and personnel to remove any contamination. Adequate provision should be made to ensure PPE is cleaned, washed and dried and made available for re-use.

Team members should be aware of their own limitations and ensure their team leader is aware when they need resting, are exhausted, require food etc.

Defining drowning

In a literature review, Papa et al[5]. discovered that there were over 33 different definitions for drowning with 20 possible outcomes. This makes comparison and analysis of data from different researchers very difficult. Consequently, in 2005 the World Congress on Drowning formulated a new definition for drowning, conforming to Utstein guidelines, which will greatly assist in drowning research and enable a truer picture of the global burden of drowning to be established.

The following definition was adopted:

'Drowning is the process of experiencing respiratory impairment from submersion/immersion in liquid.'

Drowning outcomes should be classified as: death, morbidity, and no morbidity. There was also consensus that the terms wet, dry, active, passive, silent, and secondary drowning should no longer be used. Thus a simple, comprehensive and internationally accepted definition of drowning has been developed.

Globally, drowning is the third most common cause of accidental death (after road traffic accidents and falls). The current estimate from the World Health Organization and the International Lifesaving Federation is that 359,000 people drown annually. It should be noted that transport accidents, suicides, murders, and deaths during floods are not included in this figure. Due to the lack of accurate reporting methods (even in developed countries), we can be sure that this is a significant underestimate.

To put the overall drowning figures in to perspective, here are some statistics from the US, Canada, and the UK.

United States[6]:

- An average of 3,533 fatal unintentional drownings occur annually (non-boat related) or approximately 10 deaths per day
- 347 additional people die each year from boat-related accidents, 88% of which were not wearing life jackets
- 20% of drownings are children 14 and younger, and for every fatality another 5 receive emergency department care for nonfatal submersion injuries.
- 80% of drowning victims across all age groups are male

Canada[7]

- An average of 525 people drown annually
- 60% occur in summer months
- At most risk are children aged 1-4 and men aged 15-34
- Men count for 83% of all drownings

5   L Papa, R Hoelle, A Idris. Systematic review of definitions for drowning incidents. Resuscitation, Volume 65, Issue 3, Pages 255-264

6   http://www.cdc.gov/HomeandRecreationalSafety/Water-Safety/waterinjuries-factsheet.html

7   Canadian Red Cross, 2010

United Kingdom[8]

- 635 deaths from drowning (of which 371 are suspected as accidental or natural causes)
- 203 (55% of accidental/natural causes) in lakes, rivers, and streams
- 124 (33% of accidental/natural causes) in coastal water and sea

Significant factors in the majority of these deaths have been the lack of safety equipment (such as lifejackets) and the influence of alcohol.

Anyone who has been submerged and is suspected of having aspirated water must receive medical attention, even if they are alert and fully rational, regardless of whether or not they are exhibiting some evidence of water in their lungs (such as chest pain, coughing, breathing difficulties, white or pink foam around the mouth or nostrils). Complications can arise up to 72 hours after the submersion. It should be noted that it does not require complete submersion to drown and it is possible to aspirate sufficient water during intermittent submersion of the face.

The irritating effects of water on the lungs can lead to complications which can potentially result in death, and requires specific treatment. Traditionally, terms such as 'near drowning' and 'secondary drowning' have been used to describe situations where the victim either survives, at least temporarily, following aspiration of fluid into the lungs, or if death occurs at a later time following initial aspiration of water. As discussed above, such terminology leads to confusion and should no longer be used.

The drowning process

Upon submersion, conscious people will normally attempt to hold their breath. The determining factor in ability to breath-hold is not a lack of oxygen nor a build up of carbon dioxide, but the build up of nervous impulses that commence from when inspiration stops, until the desire to breathe becomes overwhelming. This impulse can be reduced by swallowing or other movements that move the respiratory muscles. Immersion in cold water leads to stimulation of skin receptors which produces a separate unassociated desire to breathe.

It is possible that the extension of breath holding by swallowing is the reason why large volumes of water are found in the stomachs of some drowning victims.

After a varying amount of time, the victim will start to inhale water and eventually fall unconscious – although it should be recognized that at this point they will still have cardiac output. As the victim becomes increasingly hypoxic, a fatal arrhythmia will eventually result.

Further reading

Essentials of Sea Survival by Frank Golden and Michael Tipton (2002).

Handbook on Drowning: Prevention Rescue and Treatment by Joost Bierens (Editor) (2005)

---

8   Royal Society for the Prevention of Accidents, 2012

Hydrostatic shock

Hydrostatic shock occurs when a victim is immersed in water for a long period of time. The water exerts a pressure onto the body, in particular the legs as they are deeper in the water. This, in turn, reduces blood flow to the legs, causing pooling and artificially maintaining high blood pressure. When the victim is then rescued and pulled from the water in a vertical position, the pressure on the body will be rapidly lost, causing blood pressure to rapidly drop. A rapid drop in blood pressure will cause a loss of consciousness and potentially cardiac arrest.

However, the victim must come out of the water. The water is definitely the more dangerous of the risks present, and bringing the victim up a river bank or over the side of a boat tends not to be problematic for them. Most issues with hydrostatic shock have occurred when casualties have been winched into a helicopter using only a single strop after spending long periods of time in the water. In this situation, they would be held vertically for a longer period of time. They can lose consciousness in the strop, and as a result their airway will be blocked by their head falling forward. Correct procedure is now to double-strop all casualties pulled from the water (one strop under the armpits, and one strop behind the knees).

4

Mammalian diving reflex

There are well-documented cases of people (particularly young people) who have survived for extended periods immersed in very cold water, often under ice. The exact mechanism which causes this to happen is not fully understood, but it is often attributed to the mammalian dive reflex. Rescuers must remember that this is a very rare condition and it only occurs in very cold water.

As this is a very rare condition, rescuers must not allow their judgment to be unnecessarily swayed by the assumption that this mammalian diving response has occurred. However, where a cold victim has been recovered from the water, CPR should be administered as appropriate. See "Cardio–pulmonary resuscitation (CPR) for the drowned victim" on page 98 for further information.

Cardio–pulmonary resuscitation (CPR) for the drowned victim

The protocols for dealing with an unconscious non-breathing casualty are constantly under review. Below are the current guidelines from the American Heart Association.

These guidelines show the modifications to make them appropriate for the drowning victim. The sequence of actions for a casualty that has not experienced drowning is slightly different – readers should seek a good quality First Aid manual. However, in every case, regardless of the cause of collapse, doing something is better than doing nothing.

Basic life support consists of the following sequence of actions:

1. Make sure you, the victim, and any bystanders are safe.

2. Check the victim for a response.
   Gently shake the shoulders and ask loudly, "Are you all right?"

3. **If they respond**: Leave them in the position in which you find them provided there is no further danger. Try to find out what is wrong with them and get help if needed. Reassess them regularly.

   If they do not respond: Shout for help. Turn the victim onto their back and then open the airway using head tilt and chin lift: Place your hand on the forehead and gently tilt the head back. With your fingertips under the point of the victim's chin, lift the chin to open the airway.

4. Keeping the airway open, look, listen, and feel for normal breathing.

   • Look for chest movement.
   • Listen at the victim's mouth for breath sounds.
   • Feel for air on your cheek.
   • Decide if breathing is normal, not normal or absent. In the first few minutes after cardiac arrest, a victim may be barely breathing, or taking infrequent, slow and noisy gasps. Do not confuse this with normal breathing. Look, listen and feel for no more than 10 seconds to determine whether the victim is breathing normally. If you have any doubt whether breathing is normal, act as if it is not normal.

5. **If they are breathing normally:**

   • Turn them into the recovery position.
   • Send or go for help—call 911 or the local emergency number for an ambulance.
   • Continue to assess that breathing remains normal.

   If the breathing is not normal or absent:

   • Send someone for help and to find and bring an AED if available; or if you are on your own, use your mobile telephone to alert the ambulance service. If there is nobody available, proceed with the following actions for one minute, before leaving the casualty to call for an ambulance.
   • Pinch the soft part of the victim's nose closed, using the index finger and thumb of your hand on the forehead.
   • Allow the mouth to open, but maintain chin lift.
   • Take a normal breath and place your lips around their mouth, making sure that you have a good seal.
   • Blow steadily into their mouth while watching for his chest to rise. Take about one second to make their chest rise as in normal breathing; this is an effective rescue breath.

- Maintaining head tilt and chin lift, take your mouth away from the victim and watch for their chest to fall as air comes out.
- Take another normal breath and blow into the victim's mouth again, repeating this cycle to give a total of five effective rescue breaths.
- Start chest compressions as follows:
  » Kneel by the side of the victim.

  » Place the heel of one hand in the center of the victim's chest (which is the lower half of the victim's breastbone (sternum).

  » Place the heel of your other hand on top of the first hand.

  » Interlock the fingers of your hands and ensure that pressure is not applied over the victim's ribs. Keep your arms straight. Do not apply any pressure over the upper abdomen or the bottom end of the bony sternum (breastbone).

  » Position yourself vertically above the victim's chest and press down on the sternum at least 2 in/5cm.

  » After each compression, release all the pressure on the chest without losing contact between your hands and the sternum.

- Repeat at a rate of at least 100 times a minute – depth is more important than speed
- Compression and release should take an equal amount of time.

6. **Combine chest compression with rescue breaths.**

- Continue with chest compressions and rescue breaths in a ratio of 30:2.
- Stop to recheck the victim only if they start to wake up, to move, open eyes and to breathe normally. Otherwise, do not interrupt resuscitation.
- If your rescue breaths do not make the chest rise as in normal breathing, then before your next attempt:
  » Look into victim's mouth and remove any visible obstruction.

  » Recheck that there is adequate head tilt and chin lift.

- Do not attempt more than two breaths each time before returning to chest compressions.
- If there is more than one rescuer present, another rescuer should take over delivering CPR every 2 minutes to prevent fatigue. Ensure that interruption of chest compressions is minimal during the changeover of rescuers. For this purpose, and to count 30 compressions at the required rate, it may be helpful for the rescuer performing chest compressions to count out loud. Experienced rescuers could do combined two-rescuer CPR and in that situation they should exchange roles/places every 2 minutes.
- Chest-compression-only CPR. If you are not trained, or are unwilling to give rescue breaths, give chest compressions only. If chest compressions only are given, these should be continuous at a rate of at least 100 a minute (but not exceeding 120 a minute).

7. Do not interrupt resuscitation until professional help arrives and takes over or the victim starts to wake up: to move, open eyes and to breathe normally or you become exhausted or endangered.

Waterborne illnesses

Leptospirosis and Weil's Disease

Leptospirosis is a bacterial infection caused by an organism called Leptospira. These bacteria can survive for days or even weeks in moist conditions, but only a few hours in salt water. Different strains of the Leptospira bacteria can infect a wide range of animals. L. Interrogans icterohaemorrhagiae, commonly carried by rats, mice, and voles, is the strain which most frequently infects humans. The organisms are excreted in the animal's urine, which contaminates any water, including muddy riverbanks. The likelihood of becoming infected is greater from stagnant or slow-moving waterways, particularly in high water and flood conditions.

Anyone who is exposed to rats, rat or cattle urine, or fecal fluids from cattle, is at risk, as well as personnel in contact with inland waterways and all flood operations personnel.

Method of infection

Leptospirae most commonly enter the body through breaks in the skin, such as minor abrasions and small cuts. An alternative route of infection is through the mucous membranes of the nose, mouth or eyes.

Preventative measures for personnel:

- Cover cuts and broken skin with waterproof plasters
- Wear suitable PPE
- Do not touch rats with unprotected hands
- Wash with soap (or alcohol gel) and dry hands thoroughly prior to eating, drinking or smoking
- Shower after becoming immersed in open water
- Decontaminate on-site after removing PPE
- Avoid cross-contamination from PPE

The illness

The usual incubation period is 4 to 14 days, but can be up to 30 days. Usually a flu-like illness occurs - fever, shivering, severe headache, vomiting and pains in the back and calves. The second phase of the disease leads to meningitis (swelling of the brain lining), liver and kidney failure, and subsequent jaundice. Death may occur in approximately 10% of jaundiced patients. Death without jaundice is virtually unknown.

Treatment

A doctor's diagnosis is by clinical suspicion - a blood test can rarely confirm the illness in time to affect treatment, although it may subsequently confirm it. Antibiotics during the first few days will help in limiting the infection and are often prescribed prior to confirmation of blood tests.

Weil's disease is often used as the layman's term for a Leptospiral infection. In fact, the true definition of Weil's disease (the most serious form of the infection), is when the patient has become jaundiced due to liver damage. It should be noted that deaths from Leptospirosis are rare.

Hepatitis A

Hepatitis A is a virus present in feces, so it is present in water contaminated by sewage, such as in flood conditions. All personnel in and around inland waterways, and flood operations personnel, are potentially at risk. The virus is contracted via the fecal-oral route.

Hepatitis has a variable incubation period of 15-50 days. Onset is usually abrupt, producing fever and abdominal discomfort, followed by jaundice. Many infections are relatively mild, but in some cases progress to prolonged and severely disabling disease.

A vaccination against hepatitis A is available, and personnel at risk should seek advice from a GP or Occupational Health Advisor.

Gastrointestinal illness

Ingestion of bacteria that cause gastrointestinal infection is a significant risk. Sewage contains large numbers of organisms. Salmonella infection is probably the principal bacterial risk, but Campylobacter, pathogenic Escherichia coli, Listeria and Cryptosporidium may also be present. The US CDC states that, "In the United States, Giardia infection is the most common intestinal parasitic disease affecting humans."

Blue green algae

Cyanobacteria, also known as blue green algae, is frequently found in fresh water. During extended periods of warm settled weather, they multiply and form a bloom on the surface of the water. The blooms may be flocculent, or look like jelly or paint and are normally blue green in color, though other colors (red, brown or black) can occur. The blooms can appear and disappear with changing weather, and the majority of blooms produce allergens and/or toxins.

It can cause a variety of signs and symptoms, such as:

- Dermatitis
- Eye irritation
- Gastroenteritis
- Joint and muscle pain
- Pneumonia
- Liver damage
- Neurological conditions

The types and potency of toxins produced varies considerably. Although ingestion of small quantities of concentrated bloom can be fatal, human deaths are extremely rare. There have been numerous cases of animal deaths, which could cause further complications of an already flooded environment.

4

Decontamination

Working in or around water courses may result in contamination of workers. This is further exacerbated in floodwater conditions.

Water courses can be contaminated by a variety of sources, from chemical substances and biological agents in and around water, to polluted water containing toxin-producing algae or micro-organisms.

Household waste, such as sewage, is an obvious contaminant. Chemicals can come from a variety of sources, both household and industrial, causing skin and eye infections. Agricultural and rural areas carry their own contaminants.

Good hygiene is an effective control measure. Keep open wounds covered. Decontaminate hands, face, and equipment thoroughly before eating, drinking or smoking. After completing operations, decontaminate and then shower and wash thoroughly. Equipment should be decontaminated following use, or prior to meal breaks. Often, the cross-contamination chain can be broken in this manner. The most important decontamination stage with textiles (drysuits, buoyancy aids, etc) is drying – ensure that they are thoroughly dried after use.

A course of inoculations against hepatitis A is advisable for people working in polluted environments. Tetanus inoculations should also be up to date. Further medical precautions and advice should be sought from occupational health and medical departments.

Following work in polluted areas, all equipment and personnel should receive some form of decontamination. This could be a small team carrying specialized equipment and cleaning chemicals to decontaminate equipment, combined with the use of alcohol-based hand gel and face wipes, specifically formulated to cleanse waterborne bacteria. At large flood incidents, a similar level of cover could be achieved by mass decontamination stations provided by the emergency services.

Decontamination should be an integral part of the risk assessment process and pre-planned for at the required level. Inter-agency collaboration is paramount for large scale flooding decontamination.

Hypothermia

Hypothermia is best defined as when the body is no longer able to maintain a normal core temperature of 37.2C to 37.7C (98.96F to 99.86F) due to environmental factors. Classically, hypothermia is defined as a core temperature below 35C (95F), with varying degrees of severity as the body chills further. The highest risk of spontaneous ventricular fibrillation occurs at a core temperature of 22C (71.6F), but there have been survivors of hypothermia with much lower recorded core body temperatures.

In cold air, the human body loses heat through four different mechanisms: radiation, evaporation, conduction, and convection. In cold water, only conduction and convection mechanisms are available. Therefore, despite the significant difference in the thermal conductivity of water and air (water's conductivity is approximately 24 times greater), the human body loses heat approximately four times faster when submerged in water when compared to air of the same temperature.[9] Water speed above 0.5m per second (1.8kph or 1.1mph) has little additional cooling effect on the body. [10]

---

9   Tipton, M. Essentials of Sea Survival (2000) page 27

10   Tipton, M. Essentials of Sea Survival (2000) page 28

The majority of drowning deaths in the UK occur within 3m of a safe point. Two-thirds of those who die are considered to be good swimmers. These statistics conflict with the long duration of cooling necessary for hypothermia. Rather, they suggest a rapid incapacitation that prevents victims from swimming 3m to save their lives. It is likely that they died because of the reduction in temperature of their limbs, causing decreased strength and flexibility. This leads to swim failure and subsequent drowning. Many people drown before they have time to become clinically hypothermic.

Rescuers should be aware that even without suffering from hypothermia, the effects of cold on the human body can drastically reduce flexibility, strength and stamina. Strength decreases by an average of 3% for every 1C (1.8F) drop in muscle temperature. Below a muscle temperature of 27C (80.6F), fatigue occurs earlier, and force production is reduced. The muscles in the forearm can cool to this temperature within about 20 minutes of immersion in water at 12C (53.6F). Consequently, it is possible for a rescuer to become incapable of performing their required tasks, without becoming medically hypothermic.

Hypothermia will complicate the management of any injury, and may exacerbate certain conditions

Signs and symptoms

In the early stages, symptoms are shivering and feeling cold. This leads onto a lack of fine motor control, loss of judgement, and uncontrollable shivering.

Signs of definite hypothermia include loss of co-ordination, slurred speech and pale skin. At this point, the casualty will usually be capable of re-warming themselves, provided they are protected from the cold environment.

As hypothermia becomes more severe, the casualty will stop shivering, have a definite altered mental status and become uninterested in survival. If left untreated the casualty will eventually become unconscious.

Treatment

Remove or protect the victim from the environment. Remove any wet clothing, and insulate with thermal layers. If wet clothing cannot be removed, then provide a vapor barrier (such as a plastic survival bag) over their wet clothing.

Academic research has demonstrated that products that are capable of providing a vapor barrier and a layer of trapped air perform significantly better as thermal insulation for wet casualties.

Foil space blankets are designed to reflect radiated body heat – a hypothermic victim is radiating very little heat. They provide no protection against conductive heat loss (for example sitting on a rock) or convective heat loss (the route that most heat is lost from a hypothermic victim). However, they are very compact in size and lightweight in comparison to other products available.

Textile or down insulation is highly insulating when dry, but it is bulky, heavy, difficult to compress and significantly drops in performance when wet. They are not usually windproof or waterproof.

There are survival bags and blankets on the market that have hollow cells in the material which trap air. They can provide an effective vapor barrier along with protection from the wind, thus providing effective protection against conductive heat loss. The Norwegian Air Ambulance uses bubble wrap to tightly wrap up the victim, to similar effect.

If the victim is mildly hypothermic, and is alert and capable of swallowing, then high-energy drinks may be administered. The victim should avoid exercise until they feel re-warmed (a minimum of one hour of treatment).

In severe hypothermia, the victim is at risk of suffering spontaneous ventricular fibrillation. They should be handled extremely gently, and kept horizontal. Ensure that the victim's head is well covered with warm hats. Do not administer anything by mouth. Do not rub extremities.

External heat sources may be used, although there is a lack of experimental evidence to confirm their effectiveness at stabilizing the core body temperature. They should be placed on the groin, armpits, and neck. Avoid placing them directly in contact with the skin as this can lead to burn injuries.

As the body cools, the oxygen requirements drop significantly. Therefore, a hypothermic victim is not dead until they are warm and dead.

A useful rule of thumb, from the Norwegian Air Ambulance is:

- If the patient is able to talk and move themselves, then this is a good indication that they are mildly hypothermic and therefore stand a chance of re-warming themselves with appropriate thermal protection.
- If the victim is unable to move or is unconscious, then this is a good indication that they are severely hypothermic and need to be carefully and rapidly evacuated to a definitive care facility.

Hyperthermia

Hyperthermia occurs when the body can no longer dissipate enough heat to balance the heat being absorbed from the surrounding environment.

Rescue team members are at risk of hyperthermia. They must be correctly dressed for intentional or accidental immersion in cold water. However, while wearing full in-water PPE, they are regularly required to undertake land-based elements of a water rescue, often involving high levels of physical exertion.

Hyperthermia leads to several problems including:

Heat exhaustion

Heat exhaustion is general fatigue from exertion. Core temperature may be normal or slightly elevated. Dehydration may be a factor as well if fluid intake has been restricted. In reality people who have water available are unlikely to become dehydrated. Thirst is a good indicator of the need for fluid.

Signs and symptoms

- Headache and weakness / fatigue
- Rapid shallow breathing
- Muscle cramps, unsteadiness, dizziness and nausea

Treatment

Remove the patient to a cooler environment as quickly as possible. Remove as much clothing as is practical (particularly drysuits). Lay them down and allow them to rest. Rehydrate the patient with an electrolyte solution. If possible, apply cold compresses and fan them. Make sure they have eaten enough salty snacks before giving them more than a few sips of water. They may have electrolyte sickness.

- If the patient vomits, they should go to hospital.

Electrolyte Sickness/Hyponatremia

People who are drinking lots throughout the day and aren't consuming enough electrolytes in a hot environment are very susceptible to hyponatremia.

Signs and Symptoms

- altered level of consciousness
- headache
- nausea
- muscle cramps

*commonly mistaken as Heat Exhaustion as the S/Sx are similar

Treatment

- Cool patient
- Feed them a salty snack
- Ask the patient questions about their hydration history
- Hydrate if necessary

*It is possible to have Hyponatremia and Dehydration at the same time (called Exertional Hyponatremia). If you cool the patient, feed the patient and then determine hydration levels before giving the patient more fluids so you won't make their hyponatremia worse.

Heat stroke

The difference between heat exhaustion and heat stroke can often be blurred. If in any doubt, err on the side of caution. Heat stroke is a life-threatening emergency. The principle difference is the presence of cardiovascular shock in heat stroke.

Heat stroke is characterized by a high core body temperature of over 40C (104F). At this temperature, the body is effectively being cooked and severe damage to the kidneys, liver, and nervous system can result. There are two different types or ways of getting heat stroke. Exertional Heat Stroke happens when people are working hard in a hot environment and are keeping hydrated. Classic Heat Stroke comes from heat exhausted and dehydrated people who are not treated. Heat Exhaustion therefore leads to Classic Heat Stroke.

Signs and symptoms

- High temperature (> 40C/104F)
- Rapid and strong pulse initially, becoming weaker
- Deep breathing initially, becoming shallow and weak
- Altered mental status / mental confusion
- Headache
- Nausea or vomiting
- Convulsions
- Sudden collapse

Treatment

Remove the patient to a cooler environment as quickly as possible. Remove as much clothing as practical (particularly drysuits). Lay them down and allow them to rest. If they are conscious, rehydrate the patient with an electrolyte solution. Apply ice packs to the neck, armpits and groin. Aggressively fan them with cool air. Wet them with cool/tepid water. If possible, monitor their temperature, and reduce temperature reduction efforts – avoid causing hypothermia. Make sure they have eaten enough salty snacks before giving them more than a few sips of water. They may have electrolyte sickness.

General Treatments for people who are agitated or have an altered mental status in a hot environment:

Step 1-Rapid Cool Down

Step 2-Feed a salty snack

Step 3-Then Hydrate

4

Notes

4

5   RESCUE TECHNIQUES

Live bait rescue exercise, California

SECTION CONTENTS

5

Swiftwater swimming techniques

It is important for all personnel working in the warm zone (see page 172) to be able to self-rescue using both defensive and aggressive swimming methods.

Defensive swimming

When in moving water and unsure of the situation, the defensive swimming position is the default option. This is sometimes incorrectly called the safe swimming position. Swimming is never without risk. The position is a defensive one, designed to reduce the chance of injury and potential foot entrapment. It also allows someone to rest and assess rescue opportunities.

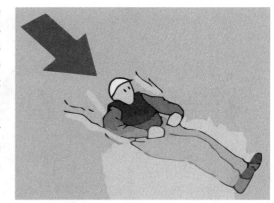

In the defensive swimming position, the swimmer is on their back with their feet pointed downstream. Their hips are as close to the surface as possible. This position helps to minimize the chance of impact injury in moving water.

The arms can be used in a large backstroke action, which slows the swimmer down and allows the swimmer to set a ferry angle across the current.

Aggressive swimming

Aggressive swimming techniques can be used to cross river currents, and make rapid progress to a safe eddy in areas that the swimmer has assessed as being low risk.

To aggressively swim, the swimmer rolls onto their front in the water. Their head remains oriented upstream. The swimmer can now use a more powerful front crawl stroke to maneuver in the water at a faster rate.

Ferry angles

When swimming across a current (both defensively and aggressively), the angle between the current vector and the swimmer's body orientation is very important. This is known as the ferry angle. A good swimmer will constantly adjust their angle to allow the water to carry them to their destination with the minimum of effort.

By having zero angle between the swimmer's body and the current, the swimmer will move downstream with the flow. If in a defensive swimming position, this will allow the swimmer to look downstream for hazards.

By increasing the angle of the body to the current vector and applying momentum by the use of swimming strokes, the swimmer will start to move sideways. This can allow the swimmer to move to the river banks and possible safety of an eddy, or to move away from hazards in their path.

By increasing the angle, the swimmer can increase the speed in which they move sideways. This can be essential if the swimmer wants to cross a strong eddy line, for example.

If a swimmer has moved to an aggressive swimming position and increased their angle, this will result in greater sideways speed, but they will no longer be able to fend off objects with their feet, and risk taking impacts in their abdomen and chest. It is a valid technique in deeper water or if the speed of the water demands it.

Ferry gliding in a defensive swimming position

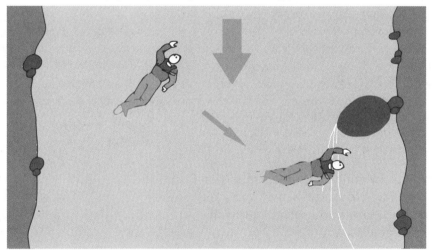

Ferry gliding to an eddy in an aggressive swimming position -
note the change in angle as the swimmer approaches the eddy line

5

Swimming a wave train

When swimming through wave trains (see page 31) it can be difficult to breathe and see. If possible, take breaths when in the trough between waves. If breathing is attempted at the top of breaking waves, the spray or foam can interfere with breathing.

Eddy line roll

A good swimmer will use the water to assist their every move. Features such as eddies (see page 30) are useful as resting places, or as a place to exit the water.

When swimming into an eddy the swimmer will have to overcome the force of the eddy line. One technique for doing this is to swim at 90° to the eddy line and simply punch through.

A more advanced technique is an eddy line roll. The swimmer approaches the eddy line from the main current and rolls over the eddy line. They need to place an arm deep into the water in the eddy, acting as a brake and thus 'locking' them into place. This method, when done correctly and at the correct time, can be highly effective and energy saving. A good swimmer will feel the water of the eddy line start to twist them, and rather than fighting it, work with the water, rolling with it into the eddy.

Strainer swim

Strainers are very dangerous hazards and should be avoided at all costs. All initial efforts should be to swim AWAY from the strainer. If the strainer cannot be avoided it is essential to try and get on top of the strainer. It is almost impossible to assess if there will be a clear route under the strainer.

5

To maximize the chance of getting on top of the strainer the swimmer should aggressively swim directly headfirst towards the strainer. When reaching the strainer the swimmer should place both hands on the strainer and try to get their body as high up on the strainer as possible. At the same time, the swimmer should kick hard - a two-legged butterfly kick often works best. This will enable the swimmer to launch their body onto or over the strainer, getting their hips out of the water. If they only get their body partially over the strainer they will need to throw their body weight forwards to clear the hazard. As contact is made with the strainer, the arms are used to pull the body up and over the strainer and the momentum generated used to lift the legs up and over the strainer.

Clearly, swimming headfirst at an identified hazard is a very high risk option. However, this method gives the swimmer the best chance of maintaining their airway clear of the water, even if they are unable to fully clear the strainer.

Entrapments on strainers can occur even in very slow moving water.

Shallow water techniques

Shallow water working techniques are a vital skill for rescuers.

There are various ways of moving in a shallow channel, either as an individual or as a team. By using these techniques - particularly the team methods - the safety of the team members is increased.

Before attempting a shallow water technique, rescuers should consider the following factors. All these factors interact, and no one factor will determine the success or failure of the crossing.

Depth

Water depth, if it can be determined, is a limiting factor. Clearly, shallow water techniques will only work in shallow water. Where possible, the water depth should be determined in relation to the shortest member of the team.

Speed

Water velocity is usually the most obvious danger. Even ankle deep water can move fast enough to knock a rescuer off their feet. For more information on water speed and the forces of water, see page 26.

Channel bed

The surface under the water can pose many hazards to wading rescuers. An extremely smooth slippery surface will severely limit the depth and speed of water that a rescuer can cope with. An uneven boulder-strewn channel bottom will provide many opportunities for the rescuer to injure or entrap themselves.

Distance

Rescuers should consider distance during shallow water crossings as such may require step-by-step planning to utilize existing eddies or other features to rest and/or prepare for the next sequence of movements. Long shallow water travel distances can be exhausting to rescuers as they can be exposed to the environment for extended periods.

Personnel

The technique to be used will be dependent on the number of trained personnel available.

Before starting to wade, personnel should consider all of the risks and hazards highlighted in sections 2 and 3 of this manual. Generally, as a group, hazards can be successfully negotiated due to the strength of the configuration and mutual support.

Single person crossings work well for an unavoidable situation, but it can be far safer to cross with the support of others. Where possible, a pole of some sort can be used to feel the channel bed ahead of the rescuer.

Group wading techniques

The group techniques, line astern and line abreast, both use the water to their advantage. The upstream person takes the force of the water while the others are in an eddy and can support the front person.

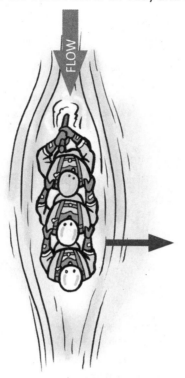

Line astern wading technique

The line abreast technique works better in low energy environments where rescuers can expect a reasonably flat surface. Urban environments lend themselves to this technique. However, it can be difficult to check the ground ahead of the rescuers, leaving them vulnerable to underwater hazards.

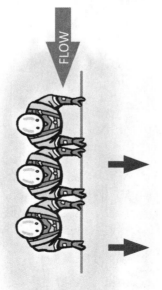

Line abreast wading technique in low energy environment

The wedge is a solid option for a team to cross, and can be used to support an injured person in the center where they are sheltered and supported. The shape uses the rescuers' bodies to protect and shelter the litter basket held in the center.

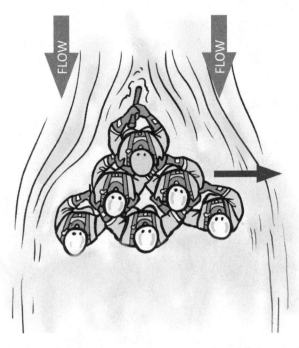

5

Patients must not be tied into the litter basket for in-water operations. If the victim requires immobilization (in the case of a suspected spinal injury), then hands on stabilization or a different option should be used for safe evacuation. Use a PFD on the patient when transporting across the water.

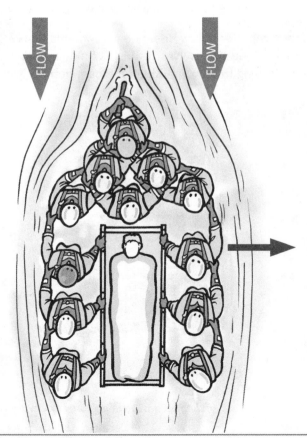

Tethered shallow water techniques

When using shallow water techniques, a tethering system may be used. This will help secure the rescuers. All rescuers who are committed to the water will have a rope tether attached to the cowstail on the quick-release chest harness on their PFD. This rope then runs back to a belayer who is in a position of safety on the bank. Should the wading rescuer lose their footing, they are attached to a rope which will serve as a pendulum to bring them back to safety.

5

If this method is used with two rescuers, then it is possible to place a victim between the rescuers and cross the channel. If the rescuers lose their footing, then they turn to a defensive swimming position, and return to shore with the help of the belayed rope. The rescuer who is downstream of the victim keeps hold of the victim throughout.

Conditional rescues - talk, reach, throw

The clean rope principle

This is not a technique, but a way of thinking and operating. Very simply, if a rope is used near, on or in the water, it must have no knots or loops tied into it which may cause a snag hazard should the rope run free into the water.

Where possible, this principle should be used with all rope systems around the water. For example, a rope that is used as a tensioned diagonal system may have to be released quickly. Using the clean rope principle, it will be easily releasable on the downstream end, leaving no knots tied. This is why hitches are used whenever possible around the water instead of knots, as hitches come undone without leaving a knot in the system.

Consideration should also be given to the size of the loop at the bottom of the throwbag. A large loop could potentially pose an entrapment hazard for victims' hands, or a snag hazard when stowed on a rescuer's waist belt.

5 Throwbag rescues

The throwbag is a basic yet essential rescue tool for all rescuers working around the water. A throwbag rescue is a conditional rescue - in order to be successful, the victim must hold onto the rope that is thrown to them. Many victims of water and flood incidents may be physically or psychologically unable to hold on to the throwbag. It is possible that the victim is actually a rescue team member who has fallen in to the water, and is more than able to receive a successfully thrown throwbag.

Techniques for throwing the bag accurately and effectively must be practiced regularly to ensure skills are retained. The ability to throw a throwbag accurately could be essential to a successful rescue. Consequently, rescuers should practice several different methods of throwing throwbags to ensure that they are able to cope with different eventualities, and understand the importance of being able to feed slack, or move along the bank to ease the shock load on both the victim and the rescuer in fast current.

There are many different methods of throwing a throwbag. Generally, people find that the underarm technique gives better accuracy, although less range. It can be useful if there are overhanging branches or lines.

Usually, the overarm technique delivers more power and range, but less accuracy. The overarm technique doesn't work very well with overhead obstructions, but if throwing from a boat or with few obstructions it is very effective.

The sidearm technique is useful if there are obstructions both overhead and underfoot, although it can be difficult to aim accurately using this technique.

Underarm throw   *Bent overarm throw*   *Straight overarm throw*   *Sidearm throw*

5

Points to remember when using throwbags:

- Before you throw the bag, assess if there is a suitable area downstream for the victim to pendulum into and to be recovered from
- By removing some line from the bag before throwing, you allow yourself some spare rope that can be let out later if needed to reduce the load or lower the victim downstream
- Shout and make eye contact with the victim to warn them you are about to throw them the rope
- Aim at and beyond the victim. It is better for the bag to be on target and 10ft (3m) past the victim than 3ft (1m) too short
- Be prepared for the force once the victim makes contact with the bag. Consider paying out rope, or moving downstream

Lap coils in preparation for line throw

The rope may be thrown in the bag, which is usually more effective, accurate and longer range. However, if the first throw is unsuccessful (or a second throw to another victim is required) coils may be thrown.

While many ways exist to coil the rope, one of the more successful methods is to use small lap coils. These tend not to tangle, and pose minimal entrapment risk.

Belay systems

Belaying simply means controlling the rope. The rescuer may adopt one of several belaying options. The method adopted will depend upon many things, including the terrain underfoot, the anticipated forces, the equipment available, and the numbers of personnel. The belayer should ensure that they are choosing a technique that is safe and appropriate for the task.

5

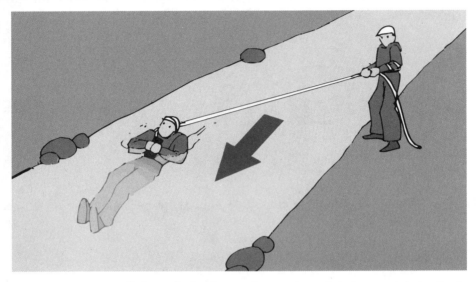

An open bank allows the rescuer to walk down the bank to perform a dynamic belay to minimize the forces on the victim

The dynamic belay involves the belayer staying on their feet, bending their knees and bracing against the load on the rope. If required, the belayer is able to walk downstream steadily with the rope to reduce the force felt by the victim. At no time should the belayer wrap the rope around their arm or wrist.

The fireman's grip on the rope - this technique maximizes the grip strength of the rescuer.

Alternatively, a static sitting belay may be used. This method is generally safer for the rescuer, although may result in a larger force on the rope for the victim. Having the rope wrapped around the body allows the rescuer more control over the loads exerted by the victim due to the increased friction. It also allows the rescuer to pay out more line, if needed, in a controlled manner, without having to move down the river bank. This can be useful if the banks do not easily allow the rescuer to move downstream.

Sitting body belay

Vectoring

A vector pull may be used to retrieve the victim in certain circumstances, but this will increase the force applied to both the belayer and the victim.

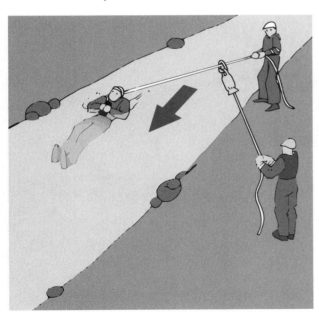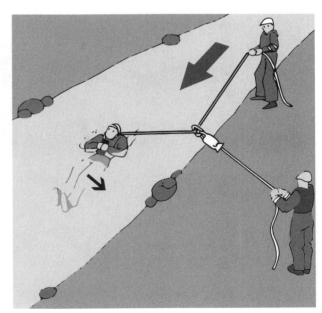

The setup and application of a vector pull

True rescues - tethered

Use of a quick-release chest harness

It is important that all Rescue Technicians' PFDs are fitted with an integral quick-release chest harness, and that all technicians are familiar with their use while in operation.

Quick-release chest harnesses are specially designed to allow a rope to be attached to it that can then be released under load by the rescuer in the water, if required.

The threading of the chest harness must be done in accordance with the manufacturer's instructions. Ensure that there are no twists in the webbing, and that the webbing has passed through all of the loops on the buoyancy aid. Different manufacturers use different webbing and buckles, so all vary slightly in their guidance for this. Some recommend just using the plastic buckle for in-water use, while others recommend threading both the metal and plastic buckles for in-water use. Ensure that the cam buckle is fully closed, and that the end of the webbing is left to dangle free. It should not be tucked in anywhere, as there is a risk that the harness may not release correctly.

The attachment of a rope to the harness must only be done either directly to the harness using a locking carabiner or using a cowstail with metal ring or locking carabiners. This is to ensure the attachment stays in place and does not clip accidentally onto other parts of the buoyancy aid, creating an entrapment hazard.

There have been a number of near miss reports arising from the use of non-locking carabiners as the attachment. In operation, the gates of the non-locking carabiners have opened, allowing them to clip to non-releasable webbing on the buoyancy aid.

Direct attachment to the harness

Use of a cowstail to connect to the harness

Quick-release harness performance

Buoyancy Aids manufactured to EN 12402: 2006 part 6

Research in the UK into quick-release harness performance in water rescue has shown a deficit in performance of 1 in 4 (25%) when testing a range of commercially-available PFDs against standard EN 12402: 2006 part 6.[1]

The authors of the research advise the following to minimize a number of failure issues that they identified:

- Trim the excess tail of the harness
- Cut off the Velcro tabs from the dorsal ring (it takes the same 50-60N load to separate the two Velcro parts as the PFD provides in flotation)
- Pull the toggle away from the body when releasing. Do not pull the webbing tail, as this has a tendency to clamp the cam buckle

When trimming the webbing, this should be 5-6" (15cm) from the buckle. One PFD manufacturer, Palm Equipment, has a freely available online video entitled 'Chest Harness Fitting Guide' which demonstrates how this should be done.

PFDs manufactured to US Coast Guard Standards

5

Standards for testing in the US are extremely rigorous for performance of rescue jackets to meet USCG regulations. Most manufacturers test their PFD's to Underwriter Laboratory Standards. For PFD's, this included UL 1191 and 1123. Among other tests, the chest harness is tested to hold at 730 lbf w/ no more than 3" of slippage, holding for 2 minutes. The quick-release buckle must release at no more than 25lbf when under 220lbf load. When wet, the wet harness is tested at 220lbf suspended for 10 minutes And must have no more than 1" slippage, and must release at 25lbf. Shoulders must support a load of 730 lbf for 2 minutes.

---

1   Chris Onions, Loel Collins, (2013) "A review of quick-release harness performance in water rescue", International Journal of Emergency Services, Vol. 2 Iss: 2, pp.141 - 154

Swimming rescues

Swimming in water and floods to rescue victims can be a very high risk and difficult rescue solution. Rescuers run the risk of being swept away. Once contact is made with the victim, it can be very difficult to effectively swim to safety and maintain contact with the victim. To reduce the risk to rescuers, and greatly increase the chance of a successful rescue, the rescuer can be attached to a floating rope via a quick-release chest harness.

Tethered swim rescues have a major advantage in that they are true rescues (see page 170). They do not rely upon the victim taking an active role in their own rescue. Victims who would be unable to hold onto a reached object or thrown line, due to cold, injury or fear, can be rescued with this hands-on technique.

A swimming rescue is a high risk form of rescue because the swimmer is exposed to numerous hazards in the water. However, it may be the only option available to the team. When the rescue is within a rescuer's capability and all safety systems are in place, it is a highly effective rescue technique.

As well as the swimmer having an important task, the bank team have vital roles to play. Belaying the rope, upstream spotting, and downstream safety are all important bank-based tasks.

The floating rope is attached to the rescuer's quick-release chest harness with a locking carabiner or to the cowstail, if present. This should be checked to ensure it is correctly attached by another team member.

5

It is important that the belayer is paying close attention to the rescuer. They must manage the line carefully to stop excess rope forming a loop in the water, but they must not restrict the rescuer's ability to swim.

Where possible, the rescuer should approach the victim from slightly upstream. This often means that the victim will have almost passed the rescuer's position depending on the distance from shore to current. Ensuring it is safe to approach, the rescuer should take a secure grip with both hands and allow the rope to become taut, which will pendulum the rescuer and victim into the bank.

Belayers on the bank need to anticipate the increased load they will experience once the victim is being recovered, and choose a suitable belay technique to deal with this.

Where a long swim in easy water is required, the use of fins may be beneficial.

V and Y lowers

As well as swimming rescues, a quick-release chest harness and rope can be used to move a rescuer to a particular position in the water flow to perform a rescue. This could be useful when dealing with entrapped victims if all hazards have been assessed. Never put a rescuer in danger of getting entrapped themselves. Access from next to or downstream of a strainer or hazard area. Due to rope stretch, communication, and other factors, this is not an exact science.

There are two basic systems. In a V lower, a rope from each bank is attached to the rescuer's quick-release chest harness.

V lower setup

In a Y lower, only one rope is attached to the rescuer's harness. Another rope from the opposite bank is clipped to this, allowing the rescuer to be moved around the river channel.

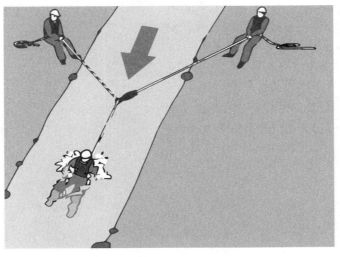

Y lower setup

The rescuer is being held in a defensive swimming position against the water flow by means of ropes and the quick-release chest harness. This position allows for an air pocket to be formed if the water does flow over the head and shoulders of the rescuer.

Even with the formation of this air pocket, both V and Y lowers are most effective in slower flow speeds. In high speed flows and difficult water conditions, a highly trained and experienced team is required to maneuver the in-water rescuer.

Inflated fire hose

Fire and Rescue Services carry fire hoses and compressed air in abundance. By inflating the fire hose with the assistance of a specialist control system (see page 67), the rescuer can create a very versatile piece of water rescue equipment.

The hose can be used for the following techniques:

- Reaching aid
- Downstream diagonal (as per setup with rope, see page 134)
- Drop from a bridge
- Reach tool in a lowhead dam

It must be remembered that the diagonal method is only usable up to approximately 100ft (30-40m) width of river. Above this, the diagonal is too long and becomes unusable - this is dependent on the speed of the water.

Inflated fire hose as a reach rescue

Inflated fire hose dropped from bridge to upstream swimmer

Inflated fire hose into lowhead dam

Looping methods

All of the above inflated fire hose techniques are limited by reliance upon the victim. They are all conditional rescues (see page 170). The victim must hold on to the hose. This is particularly difficult in moving water.

Two of the following three methods have been developed with hose for moving water incidents. Both use a short length (9-12ft / 3–4m) of inflated fire hose. The hose is attached to a floating rope so that the hose will wrap around the victim and hold them in the loop of the hose. The reliance upon the actions of the victim is reduced, but not removed entirely.

The victim still needs to lift their arms, so that the hose wraps around the victim's chest. These methods are unlikely to work with unconscious victims.

Long Beach method

Developed by the Long Beach Fire Department in California, this method has been successfully used for a number of rescues in high speed water drainage channels.

The key concept is that the end of the hose nearest to the bank has a pulley attached, and the floating rope is fed through this pulley. The end of the rope is then secured to the end of the hose furthest from the bank. The end of the rope on the bank is secured in such a way that it can be released under load. Clearly, a long length of floating rope is required.

Lowering from a bridge

The upstream spotter moves as necessary, so that they are always in line with the victim. The hose attendants move as needed to keep the upstream spotter in line with middle of the inflated hose.

As the victim is about to go under the bridge, the upstream spotter shouts for them to raise their arms. To emphasize this, he raises his arms – this is the signal for the hose to be dropped onto the water. Once the victim is downstream of the bridge, the attendants drop the floating line upstream of the victim.

As the victim is carried downstream, holding onto the hose, the rope system goes tight and wraps the hose around the victim. The whole system will pendulum towards the bank.

After the rope is dropped, the victim is wrapped in the hose

Charlotte method

This is a similar method developed in the Charlotte Fire Department, North Carolina. This uses three ropes to create the loop. There is no pulley in this system, so one rope goes to each end of the hose. The third rope goes from the far end of the hose to the bank. The advantage of this system is that the length of rope required is a lot less. However, the forces experienced by the hose operators may be higher.

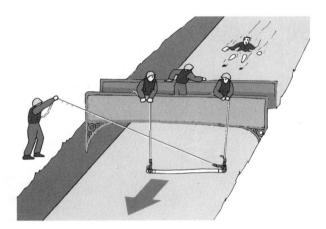

The setup for the Charlotte method

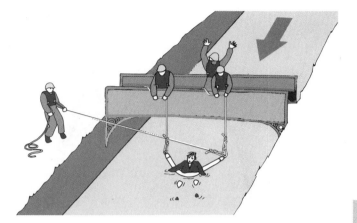

The catch - as the upstream spotter raises his arms, the rope handlers must retain hold of the rope to form the loop

5

The recovery - the forces on the ropes will be at their highest as the victim swings in towards the bank

Collapsable Loop/Box Cinch/ Chula Vista Lasso Method

The Box Cinch is a great technique to catch a victim caught in a flash flood or canal provided you can get downstream and have access to both banks. Chula Vista Fire in California was able to capture victims on two different occasions with less than 3 minutes on scene before presented with a victim. In both cases, the victim was lassoed effectively and released on scene with only minor bruising. The chance for survival of either of these victims without this technique would have been negligible. It has been proven effective in channels 60 feet (20 meters) or less across, and can be set up in seconds.

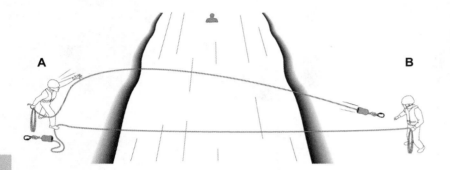

Both rescuers A and B attach a carabiner to their throwbags. Rescuer A throws her throwbag across the water to B. And, Rescuer B throws his throwbag across to Rescuer A.

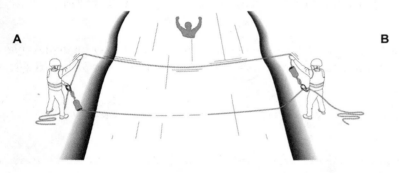

Rescuer A clips the carabiner on the throwbag that was thrown to her onto her throwbag line. Rescue B does the same. Both rescuers A and B hold one of the lines down at water level and the other one high over the water They yell at the victim who is approaching from upstream to "grab the line." They shake the line wildly to get the victim to raise his arms to grab the high line. Instead they keep it just out of his reach and drop it immediately behind him.

Rescuers A and B pull fast and hard on their lines to cinch around the victim's torso.

Once the victim is cinched, Rescuers A and B quickly move upstream as far as their lines permit. Rescuer A then lets out her line and Rescuer B pendulums the victim to shore.

Line crossing methods

It may be necessary to get a rope from one side of a channel to the other, in order to carry out some forms of rope-based rescue, and to enable teams to cross a channel. Often, this can be the most difficult part of the whole rescue. For efficient time management, this needs to be started early as it will take a lot of time. Also, once a rope is across the channel, it should be among the last things to come down. Lots of time will be wasted if a rope has to be crossed again.

There are many ways this may be done:

- Use of bridge
- Throwing
- Wading
- By boat
- Swimming
- Rope launcher
- Catapults, bows and guns

It may be necessary to first send over a small diameter rope as a messenger line, to facilitate getting a larger rope over.

It should also be considered that while getting a rope across a large expanse of water may be achievable, it may still be impractical to work over such a distance, as tensioning it or building it into a rope-based system will be very difficult.

While relatively straightforward in theory, all the above line crossing techniques require practice by all team members.

If a rope is to be crossed by either swimming or use of a boat, then the initial rope transported by the boat or swimmer must be quickly releasable and a floating rope. There should be someone to receive the boat or swimmer, and once this is across the channel, it can be used to pull over any non-floating ropes that need to span the channel.

There are several rope-based systems which can be used for providing support during shallow water crossings, or perhaps more usefully to transport equipment. These are commonly known as the pendulum system and the continuous loop system. Each has advantages and disadvantages. It should be reinforced that these are for use in shallow water environments only and that nobody should be tied into these systems. If a rope is to be attached to a person in the water, the only method is to use a clean rope attached to the quick-release chest harness on their PFD.

Pendulum system

This system uses two separate throwbags or lengths of floating rope to help rescuers cross a channel or access a midstream object in a shallow water environment. The advantage is that the system maintains clean rope, but it can be a little more complex to operate. If the wrong rope is let go, it can break down and need to be rebuilt.

These initial two stages of setup are commonly used for setting up other rope-based systems, such as tensioned diagonals and boat tethers. The first rescuer will wade across, in order to get the first rope across the channel. Often this first stage is the most difficult part of the whole sequence.

As with the setup, often the breakdown of this system is used to get the final rescuer across a channel at the end of a tensioned diagonal and other rope systems.

5

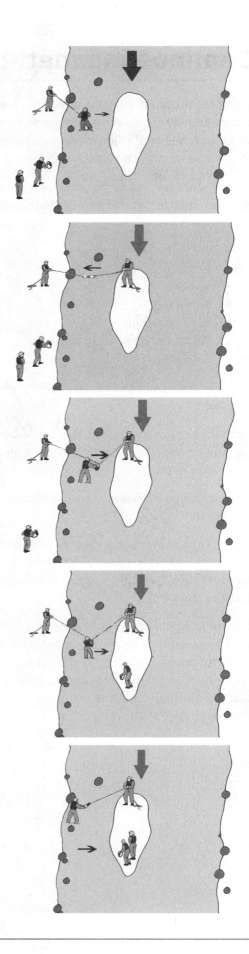

Continuous loop

This system should only be used in low-energy environments where the ropes aren't required for support. It uses a length of floating rope tied to make a loop. It can also be made from a number of throwbags tied together. It needs to be operated with caution and nobody should be attached to the rope.

The loop means that once communication is set up, it is difficult to lose, which is a significant advantage. By moving the rope in one direction, equipment and people can be moved across channels, or to and from a stranded car, etc. This simplicity of operation is particularly useful at night. A general rule is that the length of rope used to make the loop should be twice the distance which it is to operate across.

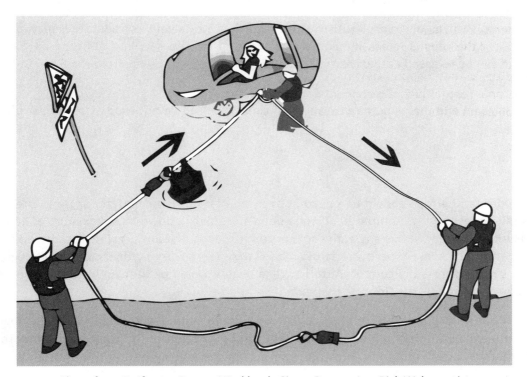

Photo from Swifwater Rescue Workbook, Sierra Rescue, Inc. Rick Weber artist

Tensioned diagonals

Tensioned diagonal rope systems can be used for:

- Crossing rivers, channels and flooded streets
- Accessing mid-channel features, including cars in the water
- Evacuating from trapped boats to the bank
- Accessing entrapped victims

This is a technique using a rope tensioned at an angle to the current vector. People and equipment attached to the rope will move down the rope and across the channel simply due to the force of water.

In some situations, such as a channel with floating debris, a key safety consideration may be that the downstream end of the rope is releasable and a clean rope. If anyone gets into difficulty on the rope the downstream end can be released easily. They will then move downstream, away from the rope, to be rescued by downstream backup.

Creating a downstream end that is both releasable and clean rope can be achieved by a number of methods, such as:

- Body belay
- No-knot

As a general guideline, the rope should be rigged at as much of a downstream ferry angle to the current as possible. This minimizes the force on the rope when people are sliding down it. A maximum of 45 degree to the current vector is advised. At this angle, the system still functions, but any greater than this and there is a risk of people getting stuck in a V part way across. This is easy to visualize by thinking of a 90 degree angle, which is a rope straight across the current. At this angle a huge V would be formed when the rescuer or gear got to the middle of the rope, thus stopping their progress.

In slower speed flows it can be possible to hold the rope with one or several team members on the downstream end. This is useful for quick setup and ensures the angle and placement of the diagonal is ideal. The key to this handheld method is setting the angle correctly to ensure the loading on the downstream personnel is relatively low.

Handheld diagonal

If the system will experience large forces, it may be necessary to tension the rope using a mechanical advantage system. Placing the mechanical advantage system at the upstream end of the rope is the easiest way of applying tension to the system and ensuring the downstream end is still clean and releasable.

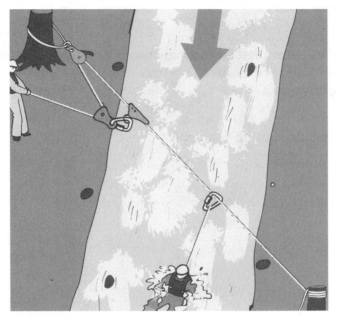

Tensioned diagonal, showing no-knot on downstream end and tension system on upstream

When using the system, rescuers can either clip onto the tensioned line with a cowstail attached to their quick-release chest harness, or use a short length of webbing attached to the tensioned rope with a carabiner. To avoid entrapment issues, the webbing or rope should not be a loop or contain any loops big enough to trap a hand in. Small stopper knots tied in the line can provide grip for the user.

The addition of a tag line to the system allows rescuers to be held in place to effect a rescue or to recover equipment back upstream. Extreme caution must be used to manage the tag line in the current.

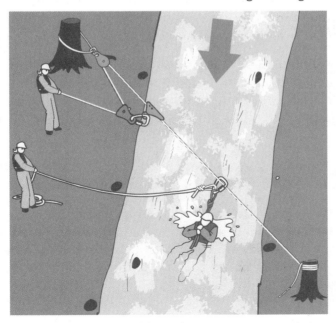

Tensioned diagonal, using a recoverable tag line to transport people instead of a cowstail

People and equipment entrapments

A victim trapped by part or the whole of their body, and held in place by force of water, unable to release themselves, presents a very difficult rescue situation.

Time is a critical factor in these rescues. Victims of foot entrapments in flowing water often have little or no time in which they are able to keep their heads above water. Even if the victim is trapped with their head above water, they will quickly succumb to the effects of cold water immersion – more dramatically so if they are not wearing specialist equipment such as a drysuit or wetsuit.

There are various forms of entrapment. These include:

- Foot entrapments
- Body entrapments
- Strainers
- Boat wraps
- Kayak and canoe pins

The priorities, as always, are:

- Self
- Team
- Victim

The stages, as always, are:

- Locate the victim
- Access the victim
- Stabilize the situation
- Transport to safety

Due to the time-critical nature of the incident, rescuers may be tempted to put themselves in danger to resolve the situation. An assessment of hazards must be done before rescue attempts begin. Due to the urgency of the situation and the numerous methods of resolving it, the team leader must gain control and communicate the action plan to all team members.

The priority is stabilizing the situation - that is, maintain the victim's airway, in effect buying time for the rescuers. This is most effectively performed with hands on stabilization of the victim from downstream of the entrapment. This may involve shallow water crossing if the channel is shallow enough.

Generally, the lowest risk method of stabilization is getting a supporting rope to the victim. This will probably only be effective in relatively narrow channels. It is difficult (if not impossible) to do this if the victim is unable to help in getting the rope under their body or to hold onto it. Once a support rope is established, it may be possible to use this to send out a floating object or a pole to the entrapment victim. This may help provide additional support to the victim.

Moving upstream allows the maximum pulling force to be applied

Stabilization line forces

Ideally, when using a stabilization line for an entrapment, the angle of the line should be as small as possible. This will exert the minimum force on the rescuers. For example, if the rescuers are trying to free a 100kg load and the line is at 160°, each rescuer will actually be pulling a 288kg load - 288% the size of the load, not including the force of the water. If the rescuers move upstream, closing the angle to 45°, they will each be pulling a 54kg load (54% the size of the load).

Basically, the tighter the angle, the lighter the load.

The weight exerted on each rescuer by a 100kg load, ignoring the force of the water is:

175° - 1,146kg (1,146%)   90° - 71kg (71%)

160° - 288kg (288%)   45° - 54kg (54%)

120° - 100kg (100%)   0° - 50kg (50%)

The formula for calculating the force is F= (w x 0.5) / cos (a x 0.5), where F is the force, w is the load and a is the angle.

Entrapment techniques

Anecdotal evidence suggests that most successful foot and body entrapment rescues are a result of a hands-on rescue. In other words, the rescuer(s) enters the water, makes contact with the victim and supports them to allow the entrapment to be released. This can be a very high risk solution, especially as the rescuer(s) may be exposed to the same entrapment hazard. The level of risk can potentially be reduced by:

- Tethering the rescuer using a quick-release chest harness
- Team shallow water techniques (such as the wedge)
- Poles, paddles etc to provide support to rescuers

Approaching the victim from upstream has the risk of the rescuer(s) getting entrapped as well. However, there is the benefit that the rescuer(s) will be creating an eddy, thus reducing the force of water on the victim. Approaching from downstream is generally a safer option for the rescuer, but it can be difficult to make progress upstream to the victim.

A simple wedge creates an eddy, which reduces
the force on the victim, and may allow successful extrication.

If a hands-on approach is not an option, then there are a number of rope-based options available. These require a lot of practice from rescue teams to be able to apply them quickly, and even then they may be of limited success. It is often difficult to get access to both sides of the river, or the channel width is such that it is not possible to set up an initial stabilization rope.

However, there are a number of single-bank methods that can be utilized.

A throw rope or floating rope is thrown into the current upstream and beyond the victim. Once this has floated down past the victim it may be retrieved back to the bank. Options here include a swimmer on a tether, throwing a weighted rope over it, or hooking it with a specially designed rope grab, such as the Crossline system. Once both ends of the rope are on the bank, they can be pulled to provide support and potentially release the victim.

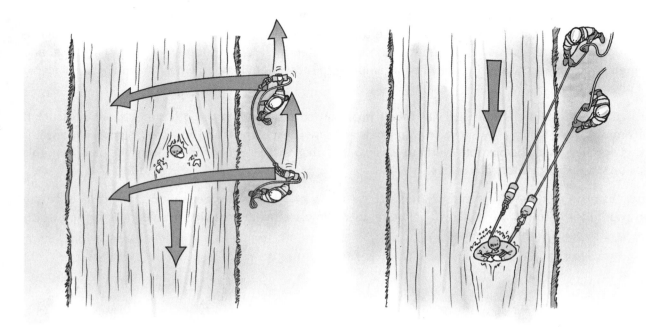

Two packed throwbags can be joined with a tape or a sling. They are both thrown over the victim - one upstream and one downstream. The loop can then be pulled to provide support.

The clean end of one throwbag can be tied to the loop on the bag of another. The rescuer with the first throwbag runs upstream, letting the rope fall from the bag. The rescuer with the packed bag is positioned downstream of the victim and throws their packed bag high over the victim.

All the previous options will be most successful if they are applied as soon as possible, and if the victim has their head up and is able to assist in their own rescue.

All of the previous methods only put a loop around the victim - there are no cinches. With an uncontrolled cinch, it is possible to put a huge amount of force through the line and further injure the victim. Controllable cinches do not have the same issue, but they are complicated to setup and require a lot of personnel and equipment. Cinches can be very useful when attempting to recover equipment, where there are no concerns about physical injury.

A quick-release chest harness can be a vital tool in dealing with entrapments for both the victim and rescuer. If the victim is wearing a buoyancy aid fitted with a quick-release chest harness and cowstail (as many whitewater kayakers do) then it may be possible for them to clip a throwbag that has been thrown from the bank onto this to provide support and potentially release them.

Rescuers can use a quick-release chest harness to setup a V or Y lower in order to lower the rescuer to the victim under control from both banks. Once the rescuer is in place behind the victim, an eddy is formed which can be used to assist with the release.

5

Litter management - low angle

Rescuers may find themselves carrying a stretcher or litter across flat or gently sloping ground. Low angle slopes are defined as those less than 30 degrees. This is generally a slope where a person is still able to walk up with care and effort, but they will not come tumbling down should they slip. However, rescuers must still be careful when carrying patients over this ground and treat it with respect.

Techniques for controlling a litter are:

Talus belay

Talus belay moving uphill

This system works well, as the litter is secured using a rope belay. The belayers do have to work quickly to maintain progress. Obviously, this method requires conveniently placed anchors. Effective communications are essential to ensure that the stretcher always has at least one belay in place. At no point should the stretcher be without a belay.

Caterpillar

Here the rescuers move up or down the slope, or past obstacles, while not holding the litter. This reduces the chance of the stretcher being dropped, and also reduces the risk of injury to a rescuer. The litter is slid through their hands when they are in position, similar to a conveyor belt.

Change of direction

Often it is more convenient to manage the rope on a path or road running along the watercourse at the top of the bank. By using a change of direction, the hauler can move easily along the path at 90° to the direction of travel of the load as it ascends the bank. A simple 2:1 mechanical advantage system and a brake Prusik can also be incorporated if needed.

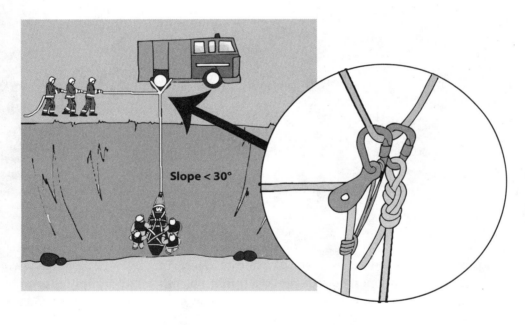

Slope < 30°

Change of direction with 2:1 MA

Notes

5

6   BOATS

Paddle boat handling, Rescue 3 Europe Technical Rescue Conference 2013, Cardiff, UK   *Photo*: Keith Dudhnath

SECTION CONTENTS

6

Paddle boat handling

In a water rescue, a boat can be one of the most useful tools at the rescuer's disposal. However, the wrong boat used in the wrong environment, or even the right boat used by an inexperienced crew, can lead to the rescue team being put in danger, or needing rescue.

It is important that any rescue team chooses craft that are transportable, dependable, and appropriate for the type of environment in which they are to be used.

Teams should receive Swiftwater and Flood Rescue Boat Operator (SFRBO) training after their Swiftwater and Flood Rescue Technician (SRT) training if they are to use powered rescue boats in the future. Rescue 3 also offers a dedicated Swiftwater Paddle Boat Handling (SPBH) course that builds upon the introductory session delivered in a Swiftwater and Flood Rescue Technician (SRT) course.

It is then essential for the crew to ensure that they get adequate practice with their chosen craft to develop experience and judgment. Only with all the above in place will any boat be a valuable asset to the team. Without the above, any boat will be at best a hindrance, at worst a potentially life threatening device.

For more information on boat types, see page 68.

Paddling a boat

The traditional method of paddling a whitewater raft is with one experienced guide and a crew usually made up of at least four less experienced people. The guide would issue commands and their decision would be final. Commands such as all forward, all back, left turn, and right turn, would be used to maneuver the boat downstream.

As a rescue team, it is much more common for a boat to be R2ed or R4ed, which basically means there would only be 2 or 4 paddlers in the boat. In this scenario, the crew have to work together and make decisions as a group. If one member of crew is more experienced than the others, they may still make some of the route-finding decisions, and call out commands, but if all paddlers know the objective and are experienced, they tend to paddle together to achieve that objective.

Boat handling

Understanding the hydrology is essential if you wish to control a boat in moving water. Learning to read a river is the key to effective boat handling. Whether water is running over a natural river bed or down a flooded urban street, the river features that form, such as waves, hydraulics and eddies are universal. The boat handling skills that are needed to effect a successful rescue are the same.

The hydrology of the future water (the water the boat is about to travel into) is going to massively dictate the future direction of the boat. It is essential that this is taken into consideration when planning the next move.

The three key elements to proficient boat handling are speed, angle and trim. With all three elements used and balanced effectively, whitewater can be run safely and efficiently.

Speed

This can relate to both the speed of the water and the speed of the boat - and, more importantly, the difference between the two (speed over water versus speed over ground). For example, when ferry gliding the boat has very little (if any) speed over ground, but may have considerable speed over water.

6

Another example is the speed required to travel through a hydraulic. If the boat is too slow, it will stall and possibly flip. More speed is required in order to punch through the powerful recirculation of the hydraulic feature. In order for the boat crew to retain control of the boat, it must be traveling either faster or slower than the water to retain directional control. Otherwise, the boat will simply float down the channel under the control of the water.

Angle

The angle of the boat in relation to the current vector determines which direction the boat is heading or is about to head. To use ferry gliding as an example again, the closer the angle of the boat to the direction of flow, the slower or more controlled the ferry glide would be.

Trim

In the flowing water environment, correct application of trim (or edging the boat) can make the difference between a successful ferry and a complete capsize. By placing the crew's weight on the downstream side of the boat (edging), it presents more of the bottom of the boat to the flow. This has the double benefit of increasing the speed of the ferry and preventing the water from swamping over the upstream side of the boat, potentially capsizing. If the boat is incorrectly trimmed, with too much weight in the bow, there would be a greater possibility of water swamping the boat. This would also make steering the boat difficult, due to the effect of the water on the bow.

As can be seen from the previous three examples of ferry gliding, all three elements of speed, angle and trim seamlessly combine to effect a successful ferry. It is this seamless integration of techniques that make up every successful rescue.

Ferry gliding

This is without a doubt one of the most important skills to master when on any form of moving water. At its simplest, it is a method of moving across the current without moving downstream.

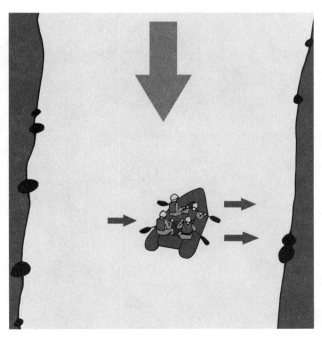

Forward ferry gliding across the flow

The boat can be pointing either up or downstream, although more power can be applied while paddling forward. There is less chance of water coming over the bow than over a transom (depending on type of boat used). As already mentioned, speed of the water dictates how much power must be applied to maintain the ferry, and the angle and trim are constantly being adjusted by the helm and crew, to ensure that the boat does not swamp and moves in a controlled manner across the flow.

Imagine a victim has tried to cross a flooded road. Their car has become swamped and they are now sitting on the roof of the car awaiting rescue.

One of the simplest and quickest methods of rescue is for the boat to cross from an eddy on a level with the car by applying the correct levels of power or speed. The crew must constantly adjust trim and tweak the angle of approach. The boat can move across to the car by holding station in the flow, and the victim can enter the boat. The boat then takes the opposite ferry angle and returns to the eddy that they started from.

Breaking out and breaking in

These are the terms used for entering the flow (breaking in) and exiting the flow (breaking out). There is never one correct technique, but the seamless combination of speed, angle and trim are essential.

Dynamic break out

For a dynamic break out, it is important to know the water and individual eddies, as the speed at which you enter the eddy can be great. If there are submerged rocks in the water or debris in the eddy, then at best there will be a large repair bill! You must choose your eddy in plenty of time as you move downstream. You then need to accelerate towards the top of the eddy with the boat at about a 45° angle.

As the boat crosses the eddy line, the crew need to position their weight on the inside of the turn. This enables the boat to carve a turn into the eddy, and prevents the downstream tube from dipping and potentially flipping. As soon as the boat is in the eddy, the crew need to return to their original positions. The act of the bow entering the slow moving water helps turn the boat quickly, but does make this a dynamic maneuver, and depends on a lot of crew cooperation and awareness. With practice and knowledge of local areas, it is very effective.

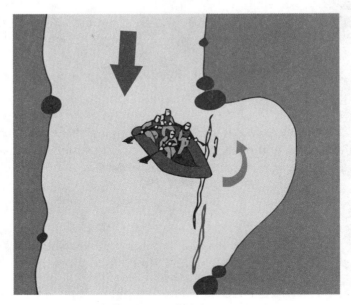

Dynamic break out

Ferrying out

A more controlled method of breaking out can be accomplished by turning in plenty of time to point upstream as you travel down river, and then by maintaining an upstream ferry angle. The power can be regulated to cross the river or move downstream in a controlled manner to the intended eddy. This method does not involve huge movements of crew or weight, and there is much less chance of dipping a tube and flipping the boat as it crosses the eddy line.

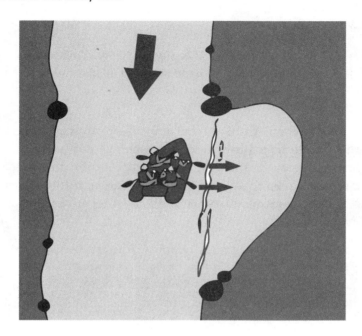

A ferry glide breaking out of the current

6

Dynamic break in

A dynamic method of leaving an eddy or breaking in to the main flow is to start from the bottom of the eddy and to accelerate upstream. Cross the eddy line at around a 45° angle, with the crew positioned to the downstream side to ensure the correct trim. With the correct application of power as the bow enters the flow and starts to turn downstream, the boat carves a turn and can continue downstream without sinking the upstream tube, avoiding the risk of swamping or even flipping the boat.

Ferry in

Another method is to maintain a steady ferry angle as you leave the eddy. Once in the main flow, power can be reduced until the boat is moving downstream at the same speed as the flow and then a turn can be initiated. This works well if there is lots of room and time, or if it is not possible to initiate the turn from the eddy. There is also less chance of dipping the upstream tube or edge.

Fade in

A third method is to fade in to the main flow from the bottom of the eddy (commonly called fading out of an eddy). Here, the eddy line is less powerful and therefore less likely to affect the balance of the boat.

Whichever method is used, an important point to remember is that the water in the eddy moves upstream. When ferrying across a river, the moment the eddy line is crossed, the water is suddenly traveling in the

opposite direction. If speed is not carefully controlled, the boat can move upstream at a fair rate of knots, usually to the accompaniment of splintering fiberglass or ripping fabric as the boat hits the top of the eddy.

Understanding hydrology

Learning to read any section of moving water either from the boat or the bank is an essential skill to develop. It is good to observe sections of water and plan a safe route through any obstructions. Scouting, as it is called, is essential if the water is unknown or the local river is unrecognizable due to flood conditions.

Five minutes spent scouting a section of water can save hours trying to extricate a wrapped boat later. It is good to get an overall view of the section of water at hand and decide whether or not it is possible.

And if not, is it possible to carry the boat round?

If the decision is made to run the section, it is worth building up a picture of where the boat needs to be at certain points in the section. One method is to walk downstream, getting an overall picture, and then walk back to the boat inspecting in more detail. This way the water can be broken down into small sections, allowing you to picture where the boat needs to be at any one time, and what hazards there are if it goes wrong. There is no one correct way. The judgment needed to make the call of whether any section of water can be run safely can only be built up over time.

A technique of scouting from the boat is called eddy hopping. This can be extremely effective, and involves moving from eddy to eddy, but only if they are in line of sight. It is good practice to ensure that two clear eddies can be seen before leaving the eddy. Using this method, the water in between the eddies can be seen and the route planned. Standing up in the boat allows a better view. Once in the next eddy, look for the one after that, and only move on if it can be seen. If a section disappears around a bend or over a fall, you must scout from the bank.

6

Momentum and drift

Momentum and drift can be used for an advantage on all moving water. This can be seen as using the flow of the water and river features to assist. In a paddle boat, this is essential - however strong the crew is, the river always has more force and never tires.

With powerboats, it is easy to neglect momentum and drift because there is a motor to get you out of trouble. To develop as a competent and safe boat handler, and especially a paddle boat handler, rescuers must learn to feel what is happening to the boat underneath their feet.

Waves can be used to cross water or to correct the position of the boat in the middle of a rapid. Even rocks can be utilized to speed up a turn if contact is made at the right time and in the right part of the boat.

For paddle boats, reacting in plenty of time and planning ahead are essential. Knowledge of how powerful the water is, where the current is trying to go, and how to utilize this power to assist, must become second nature.

Tethered boats

A tethered boat system is versatile and quick to set up. The system is useful in slower flowing water, to gain access and to provide transportation for rescuers, equipment, or victims.

Single-point boat tether with ladder extension

The single-point and two-point systems can be used to transport crew or equipment from one location to another without the need for continually paddling the boat. It may also be used to pick off a victim from a vehicle, midstream rock or from a lowhead dam.

The principle of the two-point boat tether is fundamentally the same as the pendulum method (see page 132) except there is a boat on the rope system rather than a person. The two-point setup can be used for transferring the necessary personnel and equipment across the channel.

The initial setup of the two-point and four-point systems requires the team to get a rescuer and a rope over to the far bank. While this is taking place, the boat should be prepared for the task, for example, the anchor points should be rigged with a suitable load-distributing anchor system (see page 83).

Four-point boat tether

The four-point system requires more rope, people and time to set up, but it does provide more control, particularly to the downstream end of the boat. Additionally, the boat can be placed into a ferry angle position which assists with the crossing of the current.

The key to operational success is that the belay points remain mobile. It is the only way to maintain control of the boat effectively. In order to remain mobile, the terrain around the operational area needs to be quite open so that the belayers are not restricted.

If the ropes are attached to the very front of the boat with a fixed and focused anchor point, the rescuers in the boat can control the angle of the boat with their weight. With active rescuers shifting weight rocks can be navigated, as well as waves and hydraulics. Rescuers should have paddles for reaching, or to help with downstream momentum. If additional control is required, then additional ropes can be attached on the downstream corners of the boat, making a four-point tether.

Once the task is complete, the empty boat can be sent over to the far side, all the personnel and equipment loaded into it (depending on the boat's capacity), and then it can be swung back to the bank on a single rope.

The overall rigging and operation of a tethered boat system would be the remit of Rescue Technicians. However, the individual control ropes may be operated by First Responders under supervision.

6

Boat wraps

A wrap occurs when a boat gets held on an obstacle by the force of the water flowing into the boat. Such an obstacle may be a rock, log, or bridge pillar. Picking lines that avoid these obstacles is the best method of avoiding a wrap.

If contact with an object is imminent, all attempts should be made to turn the boat so that the front or back of the boat hits first. This dramatically reduces the chances of the boat becoming wrapped.

If the boat hits the object side-on, the downstream tube will rise up the face of the object, due to the force of the water on the upstream tube. This exposes the internal compartments of the boat to the full force of the river. The boat will then be forced to wrap around the object. The upstream tube of the boat is likely to be held under the water.

Wraps can be avoided during the split second of impact, by transferring the weight of the crew onto the side of the boat that has hit the object (usually the downstream edge of the boat). The command for this move is, 'High-side left/right' or 'Jump left/right'. The response from the boat crew must be immediate.

If there is no high-side attempt, chances are that the tube furthest away from the object (usually the upstream tube) will be forced under the water. Crew may be thrown from the boat, pinned between the boat and the obstacle, or may be able to scramble onto the upper tube or the obstacle that caused the wrap.

It is important that you keep track of the crew by counting heads. If there is the possibility that a person may be trapped between the boat and the rock, it may be necessary to cut the floor of any Hypalon-floored boat to free trapped people.

A wrapped boat is a boat that is stuck on or against an obstacle in the current and has water flowing into it.

A perched boat is one that is stuck on something but does not have water filling the boat.

Before trying to free the boat, count your personel and be sure all are accounted for. Make an assessment of what will happen AFTER the boat is free. Be sure there are no hazards downstream, and have a plan for getting the boat and everyone in it to shore safely.

A general procedure for removing boats from a wrap situation is:

- Attempt to dislodge the boat immediately by moving crew to the front or the back of the boat. This can change the balance of the boat and allow the water flow to push the boat off the obstacle. Freeing the boat is often a matter of increasing water pressure on one side of the boat and/or reducing it on the other side. Pick the side of the boat that looks like it has the most current flowing into it, and try to add pressure to this side, and reduce the pressure on the other.

- If this does not work, then perhaps the crew should be transferred from the boat to the bank by making use of techniques such as swimming to shore, individual throw bag rescues, use of a second boat to evacuate people, or a tensioned diagonal. If using a tensioned diagonal, remember to attach the tensioned diagonal to the boat in such a way as to pull the boat onto the rock, in order to prevent the boat from accidentally unwrapping while evacuating people. No attempt should be made to dislodge the wrapped boat before people are safely on the bank. Keep it simple.

- An upstream spotter should be positioned to warn other river users of the wrapped boat so they can either pull over to shore, or navigate around the boat.

6

- Attempt to dislodge the boat immediately by moving crew to the front or the back of the boat. This can change the balance of the boat and allow the water flow to push the boat off the obstacle. Freeing the boat is often a matter of increasing water pressure on one side of the boat and/or reducing it on the other side. Pick the side of the boat that looks like it has the most current flowing into it, and try to add pressure to this side, and reduce the pressure on the other.

- If this does not work, then crew should be transferred from the boat to the bank by making use of techniques such as tensioned diagonal, individual throwbag rescues, or by use of a second boat to evacuate people. If using a tensioned diagonal, remember to attach the tensioned diagonal to the boat in such a way as to pull the boat onto the rock, in order to prevent the boat from accidentally unwrapping whilst evacuating people. No attempt should be made to dislodge the wrapped boat before people are safely on the bank.

- An upstream spotter should be positioned so that they can warn other river users of a wrapped boat. Spotters should direct river users to move in order to avoid the hazard.

- The Rescue 3 Best Practice Guidelines still apply. Remember that you may need to respond quickly in order to provide downstream safety cover for the crew, in the event that they should fall in and get washed downstream.

- To unpin the boat, start with the simplest methods. Take the time to read the water, and work out the ideal angle of pull. Working with the water is always going to be more effective and efficient than fighting against it.

6 Tensioned diagonal

Using a tensioned diagonal is a fast and effective way of evacuating crew from a boat. Note that the crew member is being transported into a safe eddy and there is also a Technician in the eddy to receive them and act as downstream back up with a throwbag if required.

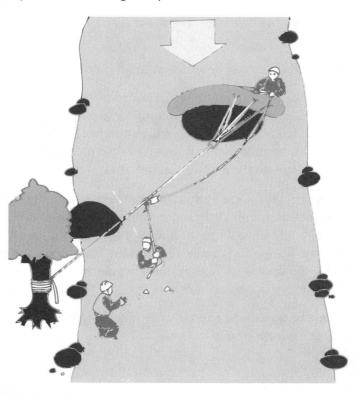

Strong arm method

The strong arm method is the simplest method of using a rope to assist. It is simply a case of getting 10-15 people on the rope to start pulling. If this method doesn't work at first, try altering the angle of pull. Remember, a 14 foot boat full of water weighs over a ton. The goal is to change the shape of the boat, or the way the current flows into it.

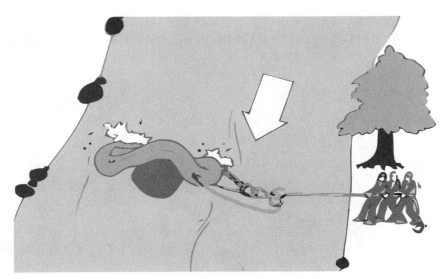

6

Strong arm method (with a vector pull)

Initially the rope is tensioned by using a strong arm pull. The rope is then tied off with a suitable releasable hitch, in this case a no-knot. A second rope is then clipped to the tied-off rope and a vector pull is applied at 90° to the tied off rope. The force on the anchors and on the tensioned rope can be huge. It is important that a load-distributing anchor system is used to attach the rope to the boat.

A vector pull only works if the ropes are very tight. Once the angle created by the vector pull reaches 120°, there is no additional benefit to using the vector pull method. The forces are only high when the angle is very wide.

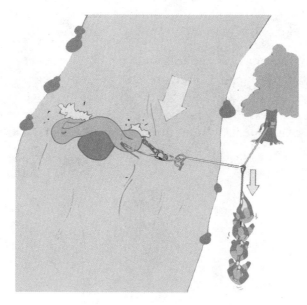

Rollover method

A rope is placed under the boat. As tension is put on the haul rope, the boat is rolled over, spilling the water. This method is very useful if trying to free a boat from a height, such as a bridge. Getting the rope under and around the boat can be a very problematic and complex procedure. This works great for canoes.

Peel and Pull

It is often beneficial to combine the peel and pull methods to free a wrapped boat. This is simply one end of the boat being peeled off the rock while the other end is pulled off. This method does require more equipment, as two ropes are being tensioned. Each rope should be attached to the boat with a load-distributing anchor system.

In the diagram, the Technicians have set up a 3:1 mechanical advantage system, to pull the boat off the obstacle. A second rope is used to peel the other side of the boat from the obstacle by using the strong arm method. The Technicians are using a spare buoyancy aid attached to the rope to act as a dampener. If the anchors on the boat fail, this dampener prevents the hardware (which is under tension on the boat), flying back and hitting the haulers.

Be very alert when applying mechanical advantage to a wrapped boat from the shore. When the boat begins to come off the obstacle, the initial movement is likely to be small, but when the boat comes loose, it will do so very suddenly. All personnel should be prepared for this eventuality. Nobody should be standing on the downstream side of the ropes or they may be injured as the boat dislodges and swings towards the bank. Crew on shore should be prepared to release tension from the system if needed. Crew, if left on the rock, could be stranded.

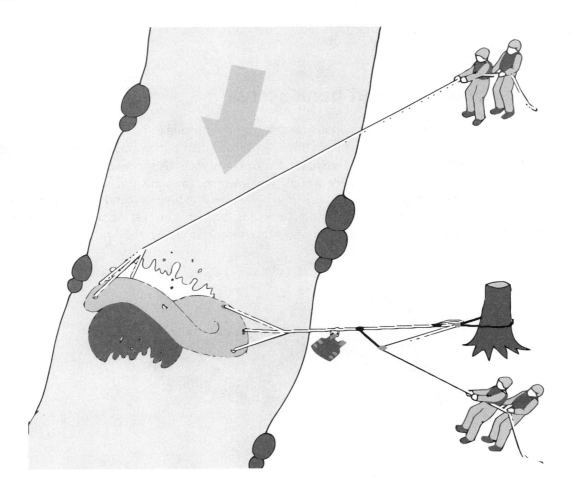

6

In–boat mechanical advantage system

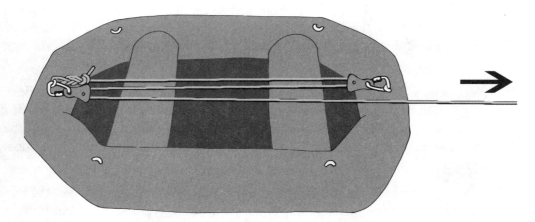

In-boat MA: For clarity, no anchor system is shown. A load-distributing anchor system is recommended to reduce the risk of ripping of a D-ring or attachment point.
However, this will reduce the throw of the MA system.

Another method of unwrapping a boat is to use a throwbag or a long bowline to form an in–boat mechanical advantage system. By hauling on this, either from in the boat or from the bank, it may be possible to upset the balance of the boat enough to dislodge it.

6

Unwrapping boats without bank access

Occasionally, access cannot be gained to either bank. Ropes may not be long enough, or the river is too large to gain any access. It is possible to lever the boat from the wrap. A load-distributing anchor is set on the upstream side of the boat. The rope is wrapped around a paddle, oar or cut branch. Using their body weight, the guides can lever the boat up just enough to start spilling water from it, which may allow the boat to slide free.

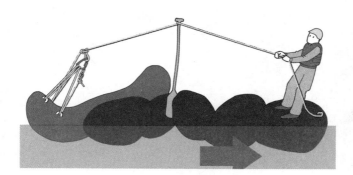

Flips and rights

Flips need not be a disaster if they are managed correctly. A lot depends on the section of water, how deep it is, what is immediately downstream, and how many crew are in the boat.

The severity of a flip is dictated by the nature of the particular section of water. A flip on a shallow, continuous stretch of rapids can be very difficult and dangerous to recover from. A flip on a pool-drop river, where hard rapids are followed by long sections of clear water, gives the crew time to right the boat and recover personnel and equipment.

The correct handling of a flipped boat depends on all crew members staying calm and working efficiently as a team. Once flipped, the first priority is to perform a head count to ensure that everybody is safe. All crew members should get out of the water as soon as possible. Often times this is most quickly accomplished by getting on the upside down craft. The boat can be paddled and maneuvered upside down. If this is not possible, the crew should remain close to the boat so that they can assist with the righting of it. A designated team member (usually the helm) needs to climb on board the flipped boat. How this is achieved depends on the type of boat being used.

For a whitewater raft, it is possible to use the drain holes in the floor to get purchase and pull yourself back on to the boat. In some circumstances a pre-rigged system on the bottom of the boat may be in place by the boat handler. If this is not possible, the use of a flip-line or piece of cord can be used. A carabiners is used to clip one end to the side of the boat, either through the safety line, a carrying handle, or a D-ring. The other end of the flip-line can be attached to a paddle or something which is heavy, and can be thrown over the upturned boat. Once the line is over the boat, the quickest method of getting to the other side of the boat should be used.

Once on top, if the flip-line is already attached, this can be used to pull the boat back over. This takes a little practice. The easiest method involves keeping the legs straight and leaning back on the edge of the boat. If done correctly, it feels like the boat will land on top of you. Do not rush this stage as the boat may not come all the way over.

Unless a whitewater raft is used, consideration should be given as to where is best to climb onto the upturned boat. In an IRB without a motor, it is usually easier to climb aboard at the transom as this is lower.

As soon as possible, either on the upside down craft, or once the boat is the right way up and the crew back aboard, it is a good idea to get to shore or a safe eddy to regroup and sort out crew and equipment.

Specialist considerations of righting flipped powerboats are covered on the Rescue 3 SFRBO course.

Paddle boat flipping

Summary

There is no doubt that boats are exciting, dynamic, and, in the right hands, a fantastic rescue tool, though the potential for things to go wrong is high.

All boat crews need to know their boats and equipment inside out. They need time to practice and become familiar with them in as many different scenarios and grades of water as possible. With the correct training and time to practice, experience and judgment will be gained – the essential tools to perform any boat-based rescue.

6

Notes

6

7   INCIDENT MANAGEMENT

Flooding in Bosnia and Herzegovina
https://www.flickr.com/photos/69583224@N05/

Photo: European Commission DG ECHO

SECTION CONTENTS

7

Pre-planning

Dealing with any emergency situation is first a management problem. Pre-planning involves examining all aspects of a potential future problem and devising methods of dealing with it.

Pre-planning is used to design methods of dealing with specific situations and locations, enhancing the capabilities of a rescue team and creating a safer scene environment.

Developing a pre-plan

The first stage to developing a pre-plan is undertaking a hazard assessment. Rescue teams cannot begin to plan responses unless they understand the location and nature of incidents they may be required to respond to.

Records of previous incidents, both recent and historic, are a vital source of information. Rainfall and river level data is also of great benefit.

While planning for a flood response, it is important that managers take into consideration the following four requirements:

- Management
- Personnel
- Training
- Equipment

By considering these four elements, in that order, the flood planning will be as efficient as possible. There is little point in investing money in new equipment if it is not fit for purpose, and the rescuers are not trained to use it. With drive from management to identify key personnel to lead a rescue team, a motivated core team will be created. This team then needs appropriate training to deal with the specific issues identified by the management. By receiving training before purchasing equipment, the team is then able to make educated recommendations on the best equipment for the task.

No emergency situation can be controlled effectively without good management of all the various aspects involved. Sufficient numbers of rescuers, trained to a necessary standard, are required to perform search and rescue operations. Once the needs of a rescue team are identified, training is needed to supply the knowledge and skills to meet these needs. The availability of sufficient quantities of the correct equipment is essential.

Once the basics of the pre-plan have been established, other aspects can begin to be identified, such as:

- Communications
- Mutual aid
- Welfare
- Shelter
- Transportation

Pre-planning can be both general and overall or specific to particular identified high risk areas/location.

Particular rivers, lowhead dams, low water crossings, and areas that have presented historical problems are good examples which site-specific pre-plans can be made for. Information to be gathered may include:

- Location
- Maps and plans
- Access routes
- Communication issues (such as blackspots)
- Specific risks
- Special equipment requirements
- Specialist training requirements
- Team response plan

Once this initial generic information is assimilated, it should be possible to determine the personnel, equipment, training and management requirements in order to provide an effective response. The use of mutual aid arrangements may be key in providing such a response capability.

As well as planning for a general overall response, particular problem areas can be identified and specific response pre-plans for these areas determined. Such areas may be sections of road prone to flooding, sections of river where river users tend to get into difficulties, or specific structures such as lowhead dams.

For such areas, factors such as communications, transport, equipment needs, water features and hazards, access, anchor points, welfare and decontamination should also be considered when establishing a pre-plan for an area or specific site.

7

Risk assessments

A risk assessment is an examination of what could cause harm to yourself, your fellow rescue team members and members of the public. It allows you to decide whether you have taken sufficient precautions to prevent harm to anybody, or whether you need to do more to prevent harm.

A popular method of performing a risk assessment is to follow a 5 step process:

1. Identify the hazards

2. Decide who might be harmed and how

3. Evaluate the risks and decide on precautions

4. Record your findings and implement them

5. Review your assessment and update if necessary

A hazard is defined as anything that may cause harm.

A risk is defined as the chance that these, and other hazards, could harm somebody.

Generic risk assessment

It is good practice for rescue teams to have a generic risk assessment for the tasks they may be expected to perform, and these can be completed before being deployed.

For example, a risk assessment for rescue training can be completed:

1. Slips, trips, and falls are a hazard while working on a river bank. This is due to the often wet and uneven ground, with a trip potential due to tree roots, rocks, etc.

2. Rescue team members and members of the public are identified as who might be harmed.

3. You can evaluate the risks based on a simple low, medium, high scale, which will determine whether further control measures are needed. By appropriate zoning, and use of correct PPE for people in the warm zone, the risks can be controlled or lowered.

4. Writing down your findings and sharing with team members is good practice and helps all team members to identify and control risks.

5. Reviewing your risk assessment is essential. This should be done periodically or if anything changes, such as equipment used by the rescue team, PPE or any other factors that may alter the risk posed to anybody.

The example above is meant as an example and how it fits with the 5 step risk assessment model and is not comprehensive.

Site-specific risk assessment

A rescue team that has a regular area in which they work should have identified particular areas that may pose a significant risk as part of their pre-plan. These could be lowhead dams, hydraulics, canals and locks etc.

Some of these areas may warrant a site-specific risk assessment, due to unique features which increase risk, or because rescue options may be more difficult due to the site. These risk assessments can be completed in the same way as a generic risk assessment, but taking into account the unique features of the site. For instance, there may be a section of river which has a considerable strainer - e.g., a tree or fence - or a lowhead dam that has extremely difficult access and egress. These should be included in the risk assessment and any additional control measures needed can be implemented based on the assessment.

Dynamic risk assessment

A dynamic risk assessment is the continuous process of identifying hazards, assessing risk, applying control measures to eliminate or reduce risk, monitoring and reviewing, in the rapidly changing circumstances of an operational incident.

A rescue team that attends any incident, whether they have a risk assessment for the area or not, should always dynamically risk assess the scene. Things can change quickly, such as water levels, light levels, debris, and weather.

Who is qualified to complete a risk assessment?

While in many instances it is your employer's responsibility to complete a risk assessment, they can appoint somebody who is competent to complete them. A competent person is classed as someone with the necessary skills, knowledge and experience.

7

Incident size-up

Upon arrival at a water or flood incident, a scene assessment needs to take place. This is known as size-up and is generally much easier for locations where a pre-plan exists.

The priority on arrival at an incident is to establish what has happened, who is involved, and where, how and what the risks are.

A tool to aid in this process is to follow the mnemonic CHALET:

- Casualties
- Hazards
- Access
- Location
- Emergency services
- Type of incident

By working through CHALET, a team leader will establish how many casualties are involved, their condition and their situation, the hazards involved, the access to the scene, the location of the scene, the location of the casualties, which emergency services are required, how to call them and manage their attendance, and finally the type of incident being dealt with.

An alternative format to CHALET is METHANE. The same information is passed on, but in a slightly modified order:

- My call sign
- Exact location
- Type of incident
- Hazards, present and potential
- Access and egress
- Number and severity of casualties
- Emergency services, present and required

While both mnemonics are effective tools, technicians should ensure that they consistently use the preferred mnemonic in their locality. For example, in the UK, the Joint Emergency Services Interoperability Programme (JESIP) advocates use of the mnemonic METHANE.

Phases of a rescue

Once the incident size-up has been undertaken, a plan can be formulated to safely deal with the situation. This will comprise of the following four phases:

- Locate
- Access
- Stabilize
- Transport

This is known as the LAST principle and is true for all rescues.

Locate

Initially, the victim must be located. They may be trapped on a fixed object in the water flow, where they can be quickly located. However, they also may be traveling in the water, in which case a search could last many hours before the rescue can be performed.

Access

Once the victim is located, then the team must (where possible) gain access to them by whatever method is appropriate. This could be a simple throwbag rescue to another team member. The victim may be injured and require a boat to gain access.

Stabilize

Once the victim has been accessed, they must then be stabilized. This may be simply getting 'hands-on' to secure the victim, or a full medical immobilization. As a minimum the victim should be provided with a correctly fitting buoyancy aid and helmet.

7

Transport

Finally the patient and rescuers will be transported back to safety and further care.

Rescue options

Historically, the mantra of Talk – Reach – Throw – Row – Go/Tow – Helo has been viewed as a rescue hierarchy. The hierarchy of risk concept that has evolved from this is far beyond the original intentions of the creators.

The variety of rescue techniques should be considered as a 'tactical toolbox' of rescue options. It is not a hierarchy or an order to perform rescues. A team with the necessary skills and judgment will choose the appropriate method for the situation they are faced with.

The order in this manual starts with the simplest of methods and increases with more complex methods, which require more equipment and familiarity with the techniques as they get more complex.

This division can be thought of as **conditional** rescues and **true** rescues.

A conditional rescue	relies upon the victim doing something to assist. For example, throwing a rope to the victim would require them to have the knowledge, presence of mind, and physical capability to hold onto the rope, and grip it tightly until they are safe.
A true rescue	requires no assistance from the victim. The rescuer must do everything, and so must be correctly equipped and trained to perform the rescue. Clearly, the risk to the rescuer is higher, as they must go into the hot zone. However, the benefit to unconscious or injured casualties is obvious.

Shout and signal

Communicate with the victim by any means available. Establishing eye contact is very useful. Always maintain a positive attitude and be encouraging. Keep communications short and to the point. This rescue can be performed by anybody.

Throw

Accuracy is important. As stated above, establish eye contact and communication with the victim to ensure they are expecting the object thrown. The object thrown must be buoyant, and the rescuer does not have any contact with it after throwing, such as a rescue buoy. As the rescuer is likely to be within 10ft (3m) of the water's edge, ideally they would be trained to Water Awareness level, and be wearing appropriate PPE as a minimum.

Reach

The length of the reaching aid is the limiting factor with this rescue. Throwbags, inflated fire hoses, ladders, and wading poles have all been used to good effect. Even though a throwbag is thrown, the rescuer maintains contact with the end of the rope, so is effectively extending their reach.

Wade

Entering shallow slow-flowing water in order to perform a throwing, reaching, or contact rescue is a relatively low risk option (for appropriately trained personnel), which can significantly increase the chance of a successful rescue. Particularly in flooded environments, the majority of successful rescues involve wading with casualties. Entering the water to wade is the upper limit of the skills of a First Responder.

Craft

Rescuers are now moving into higher risk hot zones, albeit floating above the water. There are a wide variety of craft that can be used to perform successful rescues: inflatable pathways, RIBs, PWCs, hovercraft, inflatable boats, rafts, canoes, kayaks, and many others.

Swim

Using all their skills, Swiftwater and Flood Rescue Technicians will be able to perform in-water contact rescues to rescue any victim, regardless of their level of consciousness or injuries.

Helicopter or aerial

Sometimes rescues will be beyond the capabilities of Swiftwater and Flood Rescue Technicians (SRTs). Further options include calling in a helicopter, or an advanced rope rescue team.

7

Incident management and site control

A zoned approach to water rescue

When dealing with water rescue incidents, you should zone the working area as soon as possible. By only permitting suitably trained and equipped people into each zone, the safety of the team is ensured. In effect, a safety cordon is established.

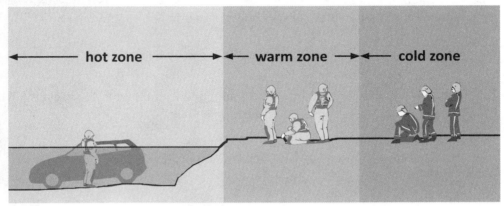

The hot, warm and cold zones

The hot zone

The hot zone is the area covered by water. This is often the greatest hazard, and must be approached by the right people capable of working safely in that environment. Rescues will be performed by a variety of methods and the personnel in this area need to be properly trained and equipped for the situation.

The warm zone

This area moves inland, away from the water to a minimum of 10ft / 3m (terrain-dependent). There is a chance that personnel in this area will accidentally slip and fall into the water. Personnel must be equipped and trained to deal with this possibility. If necessary, this area can be extended further from the water's edge due to the terrain, for example, slopes or uneven ground.

The cold zone

This is an area for personnel trained at Awareness level. They do not intend to approach the warm zone and certainly not the hot zone. They appreciate the dangers of those zones, but have not undergone the rigorous training required to operate in those zones. Personnel in the cold zone might be medical teams and additional support staff. Regardless of the level of training, if an individual does not have appropriate PPE (personal protective equipment), then they must not progress any further than the cold zone.

These three areas are the working areas required. The public are kept beyond the cold zone.

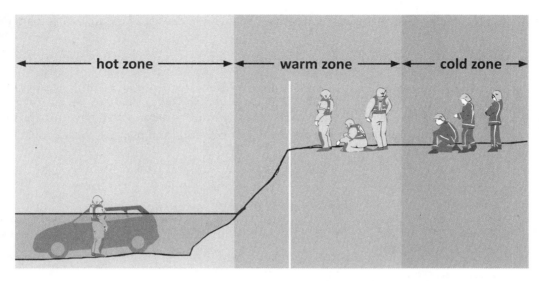

Zones may have to be extended to deal with the topography

Rescue team roles

At its most basic, a technician-level water or flood rescue team would consist of the following team roles:

Team leader

The team leader is responsible for determining the actions of the team. They will be responsible for the incident size-up, after which they will brief the team. During the operation, they have a hands-off role to ensure they can maintain an overall view of the situation as it develops and plan for subsequent stages of the operation.

Rigger(s)

The riggers are responsible for setting up any technical systems that may be required. They will also be belaying ropes when the rescue is in operation.

Logistics

The logistics person is responsible for managing team equipment, and ensuring it is available where it is needed. They may also be tasked with maintaining lines of communication between team members.

Rescuer(s)

The rescuers will be the team members who make contact with the victims. For example, they might be the swimmer in a tethered rescue, or on the boat during a tethered boat rescue of people on a car in the water.

Medic

The medic will provide specialist medical support for both victims and other team members.

For teams with limited members, it is common that team members will need to take on multiple roles. For example, the rescuer and medic may be the same person. Or a rigger might set up a system and then take on another role once the system is operational.

Once incidents require a greater level of response, then each team needs to operate within a more formal incident command structure (ICS) to ensure that it is effectively managed. Large flood incidents will require responses from many different agencies. As such, a multi-agency incident command structure will need to be implemented.

Team briefing

A team leader must brief the team, to communicate the rescue plan, to identify hazards, to confirm tactics, and to establish team roles. There are many structures and methods used. One method of structuring this information is the GSMEAC system used by many emergency services and armed forces. GSMEAC stands for:

- Ground
- Situation
- Mission
- Execution
- Administration
- Command and control

Ground

Ground conditions including site-specific hazards. This may be included in S – Situation.

Situation

General information about the situation - what has happened, how many casualties there are, the location of casualties, environmental information, time available, and so on.

Mission

More specific information about the task that the team is requested to undertake. Details about exactly what the team is expected to achieve.

Execution

More specific information about how the task is going to be performed - what equipment is going to be used, which other teams are involved, the time constraints for operation, and so on.

7

Administration

Very detailed information about where equipment can be found, when welfare breaks will take place, where decontamination facilities are, where cordons are located, and so on.

Command and control

Information about who is in charge of the operation, within the team structure and above the team structure. Details of the lines of communication between the team members, and also from the team to the command post.

Incident management

The background of the rescuers, and the type of agency they are from, will dictate the type of management that will be in place at an incident.

Some form of management system is essential at all scenes, and whether this is formal or informal, it is important to have a leader who will coordinate the rescue effort, give directions, make decisions and take overall charge. Equally, the team members will all have a role to play in the successful rescue - they will help the leader with decisions, complete their given tasks and contribute to the teams goal.

In a more formal management system, the team roles will be predefined and established. The team will have trained together and be used to working as a unit under the accepted incident command system (ICS)

This system should be robust enough to cope with not only small incidents but be able to expand to be usable at large scale incidents, such as flooding. Here there will be several layers of management in place, all with specific roles to play. Ideally, nobody should be overstretched so their span of control is too great and beyond their capability.

Below are two examples of nationally recognized Incident Management Systems. Rescue 3 recommends you become familiar with what system is used in your area. Please note that the systems outlined below are a brief overview meant for informational purposes only and that in order to become fully conversant in these systems further training is required.

National Incident Management System (United States)

The National Incident Management System (NIMS) was developed in part to facilitate mutual aid between different jurisdictions and disciplines. NIMS benefits include:

- Unified approach to incident management
- Standard command and management structures
- Emphasis on preparedness, mutual aid and resource management

Compliance and Technical Assistance

ICS is not just a good idea, it's mandated for all first responders by the Department of Homeland Security under the authority of two Presidential Directives. In 2004, DHS established the National Integration Center (NIC) Incident Management Systems Division as the lead federal entity to coordinate NIMS compliance.

In Canada, the Federal Emergency Response Management System (FERMS) is based on the tenets of ICS. This pan Canadian command and control structure provides the framework for standard incident management response and improves interoperability between all response organizations across the country.

The modular format of ICS makes it the ideal system for efficient tactical operations on incidents ranging from massive national emergencies to more localized swiftwater and flood rescues.

Incident Command System (ICS)

ICS utilizes specific roles or "positions" that are responsible for preassigned job duties. The system is built progressively as the incident unfolds. This provides rescuers with the flexibility to utilize only the positions required for effective management of a given incident.

While ICS is an efficient way to manage small incidents involving a single agency, it also lends itself to the introduction of nearly any conceivable discipline, responsibility or function as required. This means it is equally appropriate for managing large scale, protracted incidents where numerous agencies are involved.

In addition, the modular format of ICS makes it an ideal management system for dynamic incidents such as water and rope rescues where parameters may change continually.

It is critical that the rescuer be able to implement ICS in order to effectively manage resources at the scene. Comprehensive courses are available, including ICS 100: Introduction to the Incident Command System. This course provides the foundation for higher levels of ICS training and may be taken through Fema (www.training.fema.gov/IS/) or provincial emergency management agencies in Canada (e.g., Alberta Public Safety Training).

Components of the Incident Command System (ICS)

While local resources and protocols vary greatly, we have identified the key positions that are most common to typical water and rope rescues. Given that the typical real world rescue is usually carried out with a small team, we have first listed the core team, and then provided additional team members that can be added as the incident grows in scale and scope.

The Core Team

Incident Commander (IC)

The IC is responsible for the overall management of the emergency scene. The IC establishes the incident objectives, determines strategic priorities, and approves the incident action plan among other duties.

Incident Safety Officer (ISO)

The ISO develops and recommends measures for assuring personnel safety and assesses/anticipates hazardous and unsafe conditions. NFPA 1670 (2014) 4.5.2 states "At technical search and rescue training exercises and in actual operations, the incident commander shall assign a member to fulfill the duties of a safety officer with the specific technical knowledge and responsibility for the identification, evaluation, and, where possible, correction of hazardous conditions and unsafe practices specific to the operational capabilities employed."

Single Resource Leader & Team

Single Resource Leader is the generic name for individuals in charge of a single unit or resource, e.g., a swiftwater team or a rope team made up of rescuers trained to various levels (Operations, Technician, Advanced, etc.).

7

Additional Positions

Assistant Safety Officer (ASO)

If the incident is large or complex, an ASO may be appointed to assist the SO and oversee specific areas or functions within an incident.

Public Information Officer (PIO)

The PIO develops and releases information about the incident to the news media, to incident personnel, and to other agencies and organizations.

Liaison Officer (LO)

The LO provides a point of contact for assisting and cooperating agencies. The LO will assist the IC in identifying current and potential inter-agency needs.

Operations Section Officer (Ops)

The Ops Officer manages all of the tactics directly related to the incident objectives. Ops activates and supervises organizational elements according to the incident action plan, requests and releases resources, makes necessary changes to the incident action plan, and communicates changes to the IC.

Logistics Section Officer (Logs)

The Logs Officer provides facilities, services, and materials to support the incident and helps develop the incident action plan.

Planning/Intelligence Section Officer (Plans)

The Plans Officer collects, evaluates, disseminates, and uses information about the status of the incident and its resources. This information is used to understand the current situation, predict incidents that are likely to occur, and devise alternate plans.

Finance/Administration Section Officer (Finance)

The Finance officer is responsible for the financial, administrative, and cost analysis functions of the incident, including cost recovery, injury reports, and compensation claims.

Branch Director

Branch Directors report to the Operations Section officer and are responsible for implementing their part of the incident action plan. Branches are established as needed by discipline, i.e. Hazmat Branch, Fire Branch, Law Branch.

Division/Group Supervisor

The Division Group Supervisor reports to the Operations Section officer, or if activated, the Branch Director, and is responsible for implementing the portion of the incident action plan assigned to his division/group. He also assigns resources within the division/group and reports on incident and resource status. Divisions use letter designators, i.e. Division A, B, etc., while groups are established by function and use name designators, i.e. Rescue Group, Search Group, etc.

Strike Team/Task Force Leader

The Strike Team/Task Force Leader reports to the IC or, if the incident is larger, to the Division/Group Supervisor (see below). He is responsible for performing the tactics assigned to the Strike Team or Task Force. This position also reports on work progress, resource status, and other important information.

Strike Teams are made up of five like resources, e.g., five Swiftwater Rescue Technicians®, five inflatable rescue boats, or five Type 1 fire engines.

Task Forces are combinations of resources that are assembled to perform a specific task. Examples of Task Forces may be one fire engine and three IRBs; a ladder truck and two engines; or an engine, three IRBs and two personal watercraft. Task Forces are more flexible by design and are often better suited to rescue work than Strike Teams.

Using the Incident Command System

Regardless of how small or how large the incident, the ability to manage resources is crucial to the overall effort. ICS offers the most flexible and common sense approach to resource management and should be used on all rescue incidents.

The key to the smooth implementation of ICS is to be familiar with the system as it relates to the jurisdiction. Effective use of ICS can be attained through pre-planning.

Tabletop exercises (with all of the appropriate agencies) are an excellent way to identify deficiencies before an actual incident occurs. The ICS positions can be identified, responsibilities defined, and specific agency concerns addressed well in advance of a call out.

UK - Bronze, Silver, Gold Tactical Levels

The UK emergency services, these are called bronze, silver and gold which in turn relate to operational, tactical and strategic command. Depending upon the size and nature of the incident(s), the appropriate level of command will be put into operation.

Bronze

The operational level is where the management of the immediate work is undertaken at the emergency site(s) or other affected areas. Personnel first on the scene will take immediate steps to assess the nature and extent of the problem and concentrate efforts and resources on the specific tasks within their area of responsibility. For example, police will concentrate on establishing cordons, maintaining security and managing traffic. Agencies retain control of resources and personnel deployed at the scene, but each agency must also liaise and coordinate with other agencies.

Silver

The purpose of the tactical level is to ensure that the actions taken by bronze commands are coordinated, coherent and integrated, in order to achieve maximum effectiveness and efficiency. Silver will usually comprise the most senior officers of each agency committed within the area of operations, and will assume tactical command of the event or situation.

Gold

The purpose of the strategic level of local emergency response management is to establish a framework to support officers operating at the tactical level of command, by providing resources, prioritizing demands from officers and determining plans for the return to normality.

Team typing

One problem faced by incident managers when calling in additional resources is ensuring that they benchmark against appropriate criteria. The internationally recognized rescue training accredited by Rescue 3 allows agencies to provide evidence of individual technicians' qualifications, including any accredited management capability, and that the training was provided by a recognized and accredited provider.

Team typing sets out clear criteria that rescue teams must meet, so that when additional resources are called in, the incident management team can be task-focused. They will be able to select a team with the capability, personnel and equipment to undertake the task, and be sure that the team will be able to deliver.

Different national models of team typing have been developed. For example, in the USA, a national model has been adopted by the Federal Emergency Management Agency (FEMA), following separate models developed in California, Texas and North Carolina. In the UK, the Defra Flood Rescue Concept of Operations (ConOp) outlines the specific requirements for declaring a flood rescue team on the National Asset Register.

Key elements of swiftwater and flood rescue team typing include:

- Team capabilities and structure
- Boat operations capability
- Team skills
- Team training
- Team equipment inventory

Team capability and structure

This outlines the range of tasks that each type of team is capable of undertaking, the number of team members, and how this is split into managers, team leaders and team members.

Boat operations capability

This sets out whether the team needs to have a boat capability. If they have a boat capability, it states what type of boat this needs to be. This is rarely design-specific, but is likely determined by operational remit. For example, rather than stating a team needs to have a 5.5m RIB with a 40hp engine, team typing may state a team have a motor boat fitted with a prop-guard, capable of transporting at least 6 persons, and the ability to progress upstream in 10mph water.

Team skills

This details the skills that the team members need to possess. There are also requirements for on-going refresher training. Some skills may be core and need to be possessed by all team members, for example shallow water operations. Other skills need only be possessed by a reduced number of team members, for example, a team may only need one person with animal rescue skills.

Team training

This component of the team typing sets out the training requirements for each team type. It outlines the training that is required by all team members (cross-referencing with the team skills section). It will also set out the interval for refresher training in core areas. There will be specific training requirements for specific roles, such as team managers.

Team equipment inventory

This outlines the equipment that each type of team needs to have. The inventory will cover:

- PPE for team members
- Communication equipment
- Decontamination equipment
- Navigation equipment
- Technical equipment
- Boat equipment, if applicable to team type
- Medical equipment

There is obviously scope for a vast difference in capability between different types of teams. This is reflected in the cost requirements to set up and operate each team type. Only larger, full-time search and rescue organizations will have the capability to meet the requirements for more advanced teams. However, through team typing, the vital work of smaller (including volunteer) organizations can be focused towards running highly effective lower-level teams, who will be required to undertake vital work in major flood operations. The incident managers can deploy teams from any agency, knowing the operational remit and skills of the team. This eases the burden on managers, but also ensures that only trained personnel are operating in the hot and warm zones.

The benefits of team typing are not only limited to flood events. Team typing can fit directly into integrated risk management across all water hazards. Depending upon the nature of identified local and regional water risks, managers can determine what type of response would be required and then train and deploy responders accordingly.

Team typing only works if everybody meets the same criteria. A type B team in one area of the country needs to meet the exact same requirements as a type B team in another area of the country. If they don't, the vast potential benefits to incident commanders at major floods no longer exist.

7

Tactical decision making - TEMPOE

The TEMPOE size-up decision-making model was developed by Battalion Chief Tim Rogers, of Charlotte Fire Department, in North Carolina. It is designed, firstly, to give rescuers a checklist of things that can influence their ability to rescue someone from the water. Secondly, it provides the rescuer with a framework to select a rescue strategy that is most appropriate for the situation.

For many years, rescuers have used a traditional tactical model for water rescue events. This model was originally based on low risk to high risk methods of rescue. That tactical model is:

Talk — Reach — Throw — Row — Go/Tow — Helo

This model was often seen as a hierarchy of rescue, and followed dogmatically.

Using the toolbox of rescue options concept discussed on page 170, the TEMPOE decision-making model allows the appropriate rescue strategy to be quickly identified and put into action;. It also provides the rescuer with a framework to justify their decision.

Time and temperature

The greatest influence on the success of any rescue technique is the ability of the victim to help themselves. If the victim cannot help, then many of the reaching and throwing techniques are simply not worth attempting. Therefore, it is important to consider the capabilities of the victim - whether or not they have any experience of the aquatic environment, and what equipment or PPE they have available.

Water cools the body four to five times faster than air of the same temperature. Despite this, it is relatively unusual for hypothermia to be an issue in water rescue. Hypothermia relates to the core body temperature, but muscle temperature is far more important. A bare forearm immersed in 12C (53.6F) water will take 20 minutes to cool to 27C (80.6F) - at this temperature virtually all muscle function is lost. However, at this temperature, it will take in excess of two hours to lose consciousness. Clearly, a victim in the water will be physically incapable of assisting in their rescue (for example, holding onto a rope) long before they are clinically hypothermic.

Any rescue has four timed stages. They are:

- Response time
- Setup time
- Performance time
- Recovery time

Generally, the response time is fixed for any given rescue asset. However, the last three phases are directly dependent on the choice of the rescue technique. Remember to keep it simple. The simpler a rescue technique is, the quicker it will be to setup, perform, and recover from. This is a particular benefit in a flood situation with multiple rescues.

However, the capabilities of the victim may mean that the successful technique is not the simplest. Therefore, the goal is to reduce these times as much as possible, by using a technique that is based on the needs of the victim.

Furthermore, rescuers must be aware of the effect of time and temperature on themselves, as it may diminish their ability to function effectively and think clearly.

Energy and equipment

The next TEMPOE element to consider is the energy in the water system. This will determine which techniques and equipment will work successfully in this environment. For example, in high speed flows, wading and paddle boat operations will be less effective - the only solution might be a motorized craft.

Movement and measurement

Water rescues take place in a dynamic environment. As a result, controlling the movement around the site is critical for the safety of the rescue team. One of the first tasks when containing the rescue site is to establish upstream spotters and appropriate downstream backup. Also, part of that initial containment is the zoning of the rescue site, to ensure that only appropriately trained and equipped personnel enter the hot zone.

Linking with the dynamic environment in a long-term rescue is the ability to measure the water. By establishing the water level at the moment the rescue team arrives on the rescue site, the rise or fall of the water level can be monitored. Establishing communications with the local weather forecasting agency and other appropriate bodies, rescuers can build up a picture of what the water is going to do in the future.

Good communication links are essential!

Personnel and plan

Before a rescue goes into operation, it is important that the rescue team have the required skill level to perform the technique that has been chosen. There may be a situation where the appropriate rescue technique cannot be performed by the team. Therefore, any plan cannot exceed the capability of those who are expected to carry it out. A rescue site is not the correct location for trying out a new rescue technique.

At this point, the team should have established:

- The victim's abilities
- The dynamics of the environment
- The available equipment
- An appropriately contained rescue site
- The skill levels of the personnel

Therefore, any plan that has been made, considering all of these factors will be appropriate.

Operate

Once a tactical briefing has taken place, and the plan goes into operation, the size-up does not stop. The aquatic environment changes constantly. Constant evaluation of the rescue technique allows the team to respond quickly to changes in that environment. Do not be afraid of aborting, and moving onto plan B. There is little point in constantly repeating an unsuccessful technique.

Evaluate

An ongoing evaluation of the rescue plan will allow the team to respond quickly to any changes in the situation or environment.

A post-incident evaluation will identify any issues, which can then be addressed before the next rescue.

Rescue or recovery?

In any rescue, time is a critical factor. Teams are always working against the clock to perform a successful rescue. How long can the victim survive in that situation?

If a water rescue team can perform a successful rescue, using the simplest and quickest method, then this is always of benefit to all. However, when choosing the right option, teams will need to balance time constraints against the chance of success. There is no point choosing a quick and simple method that will clearly not work. This is why Rescue 3 places such emphasis on practicing and gaining experience and judgment.

In a recovery situation, time is not as critical. We can wait for water levels to reduce. We can wait for additional equipment or personnel.

However the difficult question is:

Is this a recovery or a rescue?

or

At what stage do we stop rescue attempts and start body recovery?

Some situations are clearly either a rescue situation (e.g., the victim is head up and still breathing) or a clear recovery (e.g., body found that has been in the water for many days). However, there are many situations that are unclear whether they are a rescue or a recovery.

Unless it is a clear recovery situation, efforts should be made to rescue the victim. This does not mean that rescuers and responders should take unnecessary risks and place themselves in undue danger.

Tipton and Golden[1] propose the following guidelines when dealing with a submerged victim. If the time of the head being submerged is unknown, start the clock on arrival at the scene.

If the water is warmer than 6C (42.8F), then survival or resuscitation is extremely unlikely if the victim has been submerged for longer than 30 minutes.

If the water is colder than 6C (42.8F), then survival or resuscitation is extremely unlikely if the victim has been submerged for longer than 90 minutes.

The Swiftwater Recovery Specialist (SRS) training is geared towards the recovery phase and the importance of dealing with both law enforcement and family considerations. It is important that there is a well defined transition from the Rescue Phase to the Recovery Phase during any heads down rescue or extended water search.

---

1   Michael J. Tipton, Frank St. C. Golden. A proposed decision-making guide for the search, rescue and resuscitation of submersion (head under) victims based on expert opinion. Resuscitation, Volume 82, Issue 7, July 2011, Pages 819-824

Conclusions

Floods occur everywhere and remain the greatest killer amongst all natural disasters. This presents tremendous challenges and hazards to emergency responders. Therefore, emergency services personnel must seek out every opportunity that will enable them to be a capable responder when lives are at risk. Statistically, it is not a matter of if, but when!

Emergency service leaders and managers must be just as capable of managing flood emergencies as they expect personnel to be capable to respond and effect rescues during flood emergencies. All personnel should understand the importance of response capability with regards to the hazard assessment of their response areas.

Emergency service agencies should embrace a community-based systematic approach to flood and swiftwater problems. Interoperability, mitigation, education, and notification are as important as the ability to provide emergency response and rescue capabilities.

Emergency services managers and personnel must possess the ability to develop and action a plan based on identifiable priorities during a flood event. While a pre-plan is an essential tool, this tool is not always available and must be created just prior to, or during a flood event.

7

8   SPECIALIST RESCUES

Rescues from Vehicles in Water Course, Canada

Photo: Raven Rescue

SECTION CONTENTS

8

Night/poor visibility operations

Working in water and floods at night and poor visibility (e.g., fog or very heavy rainfall) presents particular problems both in terms of risks to rescuers and effectiveness of rescue techniques. Rescuers should be more aware of their own and other team members' safety when faced with poor visibility. All personnel near to the water should not be alone and should be suitably equipped. Rescues are significantly more difficult to perform, as depth perception is very difficult in low light conditions. Multiple types of lighting are required for operating at night.

Lighting

Provision of effective lighting is critical. In particular, the following need to be considered:

Personal waterproof lighting for rescuers

A headlamp is useful as it keeps the hands free to operate and provides personal task lighting. It is not particularly useful for lighting long distances or wide areas, and so would not be appropriate lighting for a search.

A powerful spotlight will be valuable, to assist with location of hazards and searches for victims. It is not particularly useful for detailed tasks such as navigation or medical care.

Additionally, rescuers should be equipped with a helmet-mounted chemical lightstick (Cyalume). These provide a constant marker light, some of which can last for up to 12 hours and are ideal in locating people and equipment. Reflective patches on drysuits, PFDs and helmets also help ensure rescuers are as visible as possible.

In the UK, the Defra Flood Rescue Concept of Operations document outlines various colors to indicate training levels of personnel. Rescuers should ensure that they are aware of local policies and color codes.

Lighting the downstream catch area

8

The downstream area where the backup team(s) will operate should be effectively lit. This may be achieved through the use of mounted floodlights attached to batteries or small generators, use of vehicle headlights or handheld search lights. Care must be taken in positioning the lights to provide an overall illumination but not to dazzle any rescuers or victims through direct lighting.

The scene should be lit with floodlights as much as possible. The challenge is placing the scene lighting to minimize the problems of glare and dazzling the rescuers.

These lighting options may be aided by the use of night vision equipment and thermal imaging. It should be noted that thermal image cameras do not 'see' through water, but they are useful for locating heat sources on the bank or above the water.

Cyalume sticks are also very useful for marking hazards and safe routes through areas, as they are cheap and reliable.

Lighting the operational area

The issues with the operational area are the same as the downstream area, discussed above.

Lighting of equipment

Throwbags, inflated fire hoses, etc., can all be made more visible by attachment of chemical light sticks and reflective material patches. Technical equipment, such as carabiners and pulleys, are easily misplaced at night. By fitting reflective tape to them, they can be more easily seen. New developments are now available, such a floating rope with a reflective fleck built in. Lighting of boats needs particular consideration.

Training

If rescuers are to operate at night, then they need to undertake familiarization training at night. Rivers and floods are a much more threatening environment in the dark and the risk of injury is increased. Rescue techniques should be practiced in the dark, so that rescuers appreciate the difficulties of applying them in this environment. Effective downstream backup is critical for night operations. An in-water night exercise is included in the Rescue 3 Swiftwater and Flood Rescue Technician – Advanced course.

Communications

Reduced visibility can make it very difficult to communicate amongst team members and between teams on a rescue site. Hand signals may not be possible, so an increased emphasis may need to be placed on whistle signals, radios, or the use of light signals (for example, flashing flashlights).

8

Searching rivers and floods

Swiftwater and Flood Rescue Technicians and First Responders are a primary search asset when looking for missing people in rivers and floods. They are encouraged to consider a suitable search model for initial tasking during the first stages of a search that would help the deployment of resources effectively when time is critical and resources are often limited.

Such a suitable search model is Robert Koester's bike wheel analogy (2008), which can be used during the initial or primary phase of the water search. It allows reflex tasking, which simplifies the thought process in time-critical situations. In the UK, for example, this approach is directly aligned with the Fire and Rescue Service National Operational Guidance for water rescue and flooding.

After deploying assets in the very early stages of a search following the bike wheel model, the incident commander (IC) should then turn their attention to the future of the search. It is wise for the IC to be pessimistic in their planning, and request further assistance with search planning at the earliest opportunity, in the event of primary searchers not locating the missing subject. Experience has shown that effective searches comprised of many agencies from both the statutory and voluntary sector, and early engagement enables these agencies to respond accordingly.

Axle

This is a point on the map from which the search planning starts. It is called an initial planning point (IPP) and may well be the point last seen (PLS) by a river or inland water body. The incident commander must identify the IPP and be able to accurately communicate its location to other agencies.

8

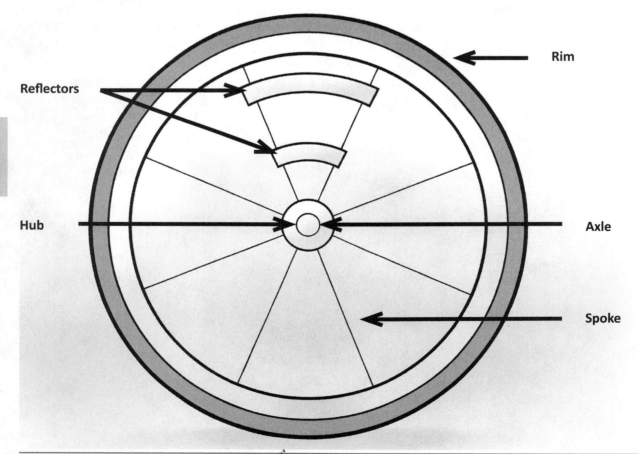

Hub

The area immediately around the axle (hub and gear set) should be searched as a priority and to a high degree of coverage. Evidence suggests that missing subjects are frequently found closer to the IPP than a distance that they could theoretically have traveled.

Spokes

The spokes represent linear features that the subject may have traveled along, and search teams can access easily. Typically during a river search, these linear features will be a footpath or bank access along the riverside.

Rim

The rim represents the limit of the search area, known as containment. When considering where to set the limit, incident commanders may wish to consider the following:

- Was the subject wearing a personal flotation device (PFD) or street clothing? This will determine how far the subject may have traveled from the IPP in moving water.
- The speed of the current.
- Presence of retentive features (recirculating water), especially those that are full width and would retain the subject, e.g., a low head dam.

Reflectors

Reflectors represent areas of high likelihood where the subject will be - sometimes called hotspots. These may be strainers, large retentive eddies, stoppers, etc. They may well be identified in a search pre-plan. Rescuers should consider that a hotspot may be too hazardous to search thoroughly during the primary phase of searching. They should be searched by specialist assets as they become available.

8

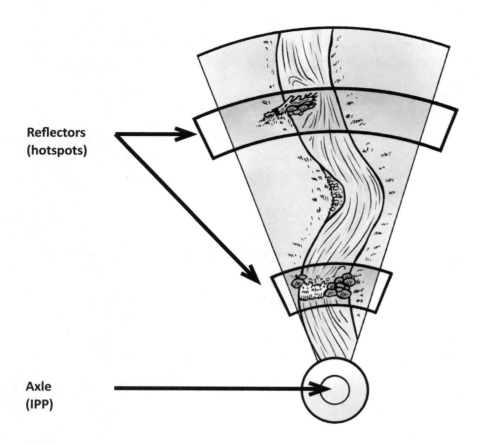

Reflectors (hotspots)

Axle (IPP)

In the picture above, a segment has been taken from the wheel and overlaid on a river search operation. Searchers in the primary search phases should invest considerable effort in searching the area immediately around the IPP (the hub). The following extract has been taken from Gibb and Woolnough (2007):

> In [water] conditions of less than 1.5 knots, searchers should initially concentrate their efforts in an area between 100 and 150 meters downstream from the known point of entry, particularly if there is a deep pool or area of 'backwater' within the search area.

Data presented by Koester (2008) shows that 50% of casualties were found less than a mile downstream when the river level was not at flood stage. At higher water levels, the distances recorded were considerably higher. The author acknowledges that the data set is drawn from a small sample population, so caution should be exercised when drawing conclusions. Technicians may also wish to review Koester's guidance for searching for victims in still water, where the search radius should be equal to the water depth.

Further evidence that drowning victims who are not wearing a PFD do not travel very far from the IPP is provided by Hunsucker and Davison (2013) who describe a mathematical model that can be used to provide an estimate for the amount of time a drowning victim takes to sink through the water and hit the bottom, and includes a table for drift during the descent.

It must be stressed that these authors have provided guidance based on evidence, often drawn from limited sources. Technicians must be mindful that there will always be so-called statistical outliers who travel further downstream than anticipated.

8

Searching rivers

Primary search

The bike wheel model provides a structure for prioritizing the hub (area near to the IPP) and reflectors (retentive hydrological features). The technician's knowledge of hydrology is very important during this phase in determining which areas of the river to search, concentrating in eddies, undercuts and strainers, but moving quickly past deep water channels and downstream Vs. At an operational level, technicians should concentrate on moving relatively quickly between areas of interest (hotspots). Features should be inspected visually from the bank, and where it is possible to do so, by wading and swimming. Wading poles are especially useful for reaching into undercut banks and probing into aerated water. Good search technique involves looking at the same area from a different perspective, often walking past a feature and turning around to look at it again from a different angle.

It can be very difficult to brief search teams for exactly what they are looking for; personnel very often make demands for a detailed description of clothing, etc., which must be managed by the incident commander. Much of this information is irrelevant and may be counter-productive as the missing subject will not bear any resemblance to the mental model conveyed during a detailed description. In reality, water search teams should be reminded and encouraged to be inquisitive and to investigate anything that is not consistent with the environment. In one example during a search by a European search and rescue team, a subject was located and the team member stated during the debrief that:

> *It didn't look right; I saw a brown smudge just under the surface. (McLay 2014)*

The rescue priorities of self > team > victim must be recalled at all times. During the primary phase (when time is especially critical), rescue technicians must be mindful of the continually changing environment and conduct an ongoing evaluation of the risks (dynamic risk assessment). It is likely that retentive features will be encountered that are too hazardous to search during the primary phase. These should be communicated to search control so that the search managers can prioritize and allocate resources to areas and features that cannot be searched during the primary phase.

Secondary search

In the event of the subject not being located during the primary phase, then areas and features that were not searched may be prioritized during subsequent phases of the search. This search effort may require the use of a specialized asset other than a first responder or technician team, or a technique not used during the primary phase. Often deep water can only be searched effectively by a sub-surface dive team. There may be a considerable delay in such assets arriving on scene as they are specialized and often have to travel considerable distances. A clear indication is essential, using a map of the areas of already searched and not searched deep water, so that the asset may be tasked effectively. An example of good practice saw a police dive team recover the missing subject within a few minutes of arriving, after they were tasked to a deep undercut feature which was the only area not searched during the primary phase by a search and rescue team. Good record keeping and situational awareness were important considerations.

Specialized techniques employed by a technician team may involve the use of a tethered craft to access and search features. Technicians should be mindful of the self > team > victim priority, when positioning themselves near hazards. Often, the secondary phase will have moved to a recovery phase due to the amount of time elapsed.

The use of a tethered boat may also be used to fine-tune the position of the searchers in large eddies or pool-drop rivers. If the water is clear enough, then a bathyscope may be used to great effect. This type of application is very useful when the river speed has reduced and the load-carrying ability is diminished.

Pool in an upland river being search during the secondary phase,
using a bathyscope, rescue sled and a 4-point tether technique.

8 Wide area searching

First responders and rescue technicians may be called upon as a specialist search asset during wide area searches that have water bodies within the search area. Under these circumstances, the IPP may be from a location other than a river bank, and the containment will be set by other land-based search parameters. However, at an operational level, all of the underpinning knowledge and search techniques remain unchanged. Technicians may often be required to provide specialist advice about features, especially searching of lowhead dams and at height over water (gorges). An awareness of the availability of specialist assets and the avoidance of mission creep are very important. During a land-based search, technicians should expect to be given a map detailing the area that they have been tasked to search (called a search segment). This should be achievable within an operational period including the time to access and egress the portion of the river. During the search, a waterproof camera is very useful for recording hazards that have not been searched or any evidence encountered. Technicians should format the memory card before use and expect to submit the memory card after the tasking.

Searching floods

Search operations in a flooded urban setting often differ from river searches, as teams may not be tasked to look for a missing individual, rather to search for people requiring rescue. The phases of search operations in flooded urban environment are as follows:

Primary search

Water rescue teams in the primary search phase of a flood will undertake reconnaissance, perform an initial search for easy-to-find victims in an area, and develop intelligence of where to search in more detail in the secondary phase. The primary search phase has historically been known as a hasty search, but this terminology is rightly falling out of favor, due to negative connotations of the word 'hasty'.

Reconnaissance may also be undertaken or supported by flood rescue boat teams or helicopters. First responders and technicians may be tasked to access pedestrianized areas.

The search for victims will typically be a house-to-house search, using shout and listen techniques, and quick visual sweeps of areas to find any casualties. Mobile and uninjured members of the public may be directed to reception centers.

Primary searchers will develop intelligence that enhances the common operating picture (COP), providing key information for search managers. Such intelligence includes the number of people in a building, assessments of survivor needs, and any additional rescue capability required, as well as hotspots that should be searched in more detail by secondary search teams.

Properties that have been visited should be marked and recorded.

Secondary search - low coverage

Water rescue teams performing a low coverage secondary search in a flood will be tasked to search hotspots highlighted in the primary search. They will typically be moving debris in buildings, from flooded streets, and in other identified areas, in order to find missing people.

Secondary search - high coverage

Water rescue teams performing a high coverage search in the secondary phase will undertake a full search of buildings. After a building has been subject to a high coverage search, no further searching of it will take place.

All debris will be removed from buildings and areas of human habitation - typically within the latter stages of the response phase of a flood, or during the recovery phase.

These searches are usually concerned with victim recovery, rather than victim rescue, and so consideration should also be given to evidence protection/recovery, in support of the coroner and police.

8

Search operations

In-water and next-to-water searching will require specifically trained and equipped searchers. Only searchers trained to first responder or technician level, wearing appropriate PPE, should be searching in the hot or warm zones.

Searchers without water safety training can be used, but they need to be carefully managed to ensure they are not operating in a risk zone. If personnel are to operate at night, they need to have had sufficient training in night operations.

Communication

Effective communication systems are vital. If radio communication can be established, then it is generally the preferred option. Radios need to be protected from water, and specialist dry bags are available for this purpose. Differences in radio systems between agencies can mean there is difficulty in communication between teams from different agencies. Recent developments include small GPS units that can be given to individual teams, and their exact location can then be relayed to the search control and hotspots and hazard locations recorded.

Lighting

Effective lighting is required to:

- Identify the location of searchers - chemical light sticks attached to the searcher's PFD and helmet are highly effective and relatively cheap.
- Allow the searchers to see where they are going - waterproof head torches are ideal for this purpose and most can be helmet-mounted.
- Allow the searchers to effectively search - this requires the use of specialist handheld waterproof spotlights. These may have limited battery life, thus limiting a team's operational time.

Search methods

Active searching is mentally tiring, and hard work. Searchers should imagine they are in the center of a cube. They must look ahead in the near distance, middle distance, and far distance. They must look to the left, right forwards, backwards, down and up in the same three distances. The size of the cube is going to vary depending on the terrain and environment. Ideally, a searcher's cube will overlap the next searcher, to ensure there is no chance of missing an area.

Careful consideration must be given to searchers in the warm zone. The environment cannot be so challenging for the searchers that they are only concentrating on surviving. If searchers are only surviving, then they are not searching. The environment must be within the capabilities and experience of the search team.

Channel bed morphology

Understanding the nature of the channel bed will help determine potential risk to searchers and identify hotspots or reflectors. The nature of the riverbed will also determine how effectively searchers can operate in the water. Use of poles when wading in rivers and floods will provide support, as well as helping to identify hazards.

Search roles

The size of a search team can vary, and will depend on the agency and the terrain. The search roles include:

Searcher

These people are dressed in full water PPE, but with minimal additional equipment. They are free to move wherever they need to as part of a team, in order to search the river bank and hotspots. They may consider using bathyscopes to look into clear eddies and under riverbanks. However, bathyscopes are of limited value in floodwater due to poor water clarity.

Backup

These people are also dressed in full water PPE, with minimal additional equipment. Their task is to ensure the safety of the searchers. They will be moving from safe location to safe location, e.g., an eddy, Normally, they will be ready with a throwbag at all times, in case a searcher falls into the water.

Comms and/or team leader

These people do not have to be in PPE if they are to remain in the cold zone. Their task is to look after the searchers and the backups. They will navigate, use the radio, and carry equipment.

References

Gibb and Woolnough, (2007) Missing Persons, Bodies Missing in Water, p41. Grampian Police.

Hunsucker, J, L. and Davison, S, J. (2013) Time Required For a Drowning Victim to Reach Bottom. Journal of Search and Rescue Vol 1 Issue 1.

Koester, R.J. (2008)1 Lost Person Behaviour, A Search and Rescue Guide on Where to look – for Land, Air and Water. Chapter 9, pp 297 – 300. Dbs. Productions LLC.

Koester, R.J. (2008)2 Lost Person Behaviour, A Search and Rescue Guide on Where to look – for Land, Air and Water. Chapter 9, p282. Dbs. Productions LLC.

Personal communication (2014), Matt McLay, Rescue 3 Europe Instructor Trainer

National Operational Guidance Water Rescue and Flooding http://www.ukfrs.com/Pages/guidance-catalogue.aspx?guidanceid=65

8

Animal rescue considerations

Rescue of animals creates special hazards for the rescue technician that are beyond the scope of this training course. To be able to effectively undertake such rescues at low risk, you need to be trained and knowledgeable in both:

- Water rescue techniques
- Animal behavior, rescue and transportation techniques

Either existing animal rescue teams need training in water and flood rescue techniques, and provision of appropriate PPE, or existing Swiftwater and Flood Rescue Technicians need training in animal behavior and rescue techniques. Both approaches have been tried and found to be successful.

An alternative approach is to train animal rescue teams to a first responder level, and provide them with the necessary specialist PPE. They can then operate alongside Swiftwater and Flood Rescue Technicians, providing specialist advice and capability. Such partnership approaches have proven to be equally successful.

8

Canals and locks

Locks are found on canals and rivers and are used to make the waterway navigable up and down inclines.

Rescuers should be aware of the additional hazards present around a lock, such as:

- Unusual water currents which exist when the lock is opened
- Very deep water
- Sluice gates
- Potential for falls from a height
- Mud and debris at the base of locks and canals
- The controls which operate the lock

When the sluice gate is released, a rush of water will create a large amount of turbulence downstream of the gate. This may be inside the lock if the upper gate is opened. A victim submerged in the lock may be drawn through the sluice with this rush of water. The controls of the lock should be secured when attending an incident to eliminate the risk of any unexpected flows.

8

Low head dam (weir) rescue considerations

The fundamental hydrology of a lowhead dam, or weir, is identical to that of a hydraulic. However, because weirs are man-made, they can have very strong, uniform hydraulics, which can be highly retentive, holding debris, swimmers and boats. If the sides of the lowhead dam are closed, then the weir can be particularly dangerous.

Man-made lowhead dams will often create full depth hydraulics which can be very hazardous. Features in the construction of the weir, such as a stilling basin, can increase the strength of the hydraulic and distance of the towback at the base of the lowhead dam.

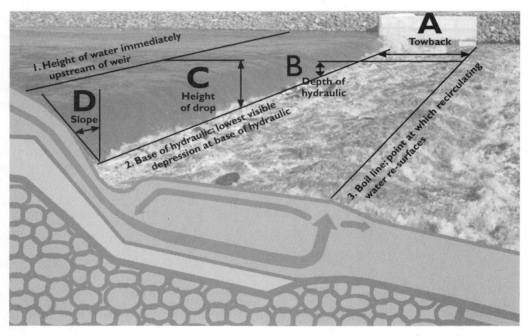

Lowhead dam cross section showing the features that contribute to the hazard rating of a weir

Cromwell Weir, River Trent

In conjunction with the Natural Resources Wales, Rescue 3 has developed a Weir Risk Assessment Matrix (below). Further details are taught on both the Swiftwater and Flood Rescue Technician – Advanced, and Management of Water and Flood Incidents courses.

Rescue 3 - Environment Agency weir risk assessment matrix

This assessment matrix is freely available to download from the Rescue 3 Europe website at: www.rescue3europe.com. Remembering that 1m is about 3 feet makes using it easy for US based practitioners as well.

NATURAL RESOURCES WALES / RESCUE 3 EUROPE WEIR ASSESSMENT SYSTEM

Name of assessor: _____

Date of assessment: _____

WEIR INFORMATION

Name of weir / site: _____

Other names weir known as: _____

Weir location and river: _____

Grid reference: _____

RIVER FLOW INFORMATION

Reference Gauge Location: _____

	River level (m)	Flow range (m³/s)
Low		
Medium		
High		
Flood stage		

River level on day of assessment - level (m) & flow (m³/s)

_____ L / M / H / VH

WEIR FEATURES AND HAZARDS

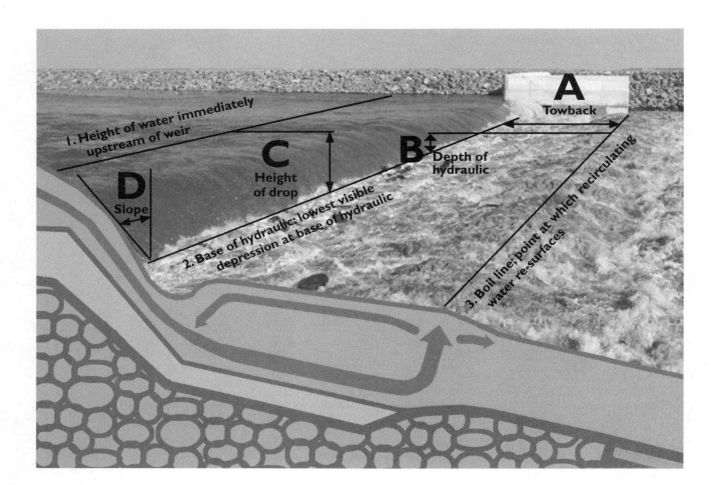

8

FEATURES/HAZARDS

A. Towback:
The distance from the base of the hydraulic/stopper (2) to the boil line (3)

B. Depth of hydraulic/stopper:
Vertical distance from top of boil line (3) to base of hydraulic (2)

C. Height of drop:
Vertical distance between water level immediately upstream of weir (1) and base of hydraulic/stopper (2)

D. Slope:
Angle of water flowing over face from vertical

I. WEIR HAZARD

How to use this table:

For each hazard, select one description and circle the corresponding score. Add up the circled scores, write the total in the Weir Hazard Score box and assign the corresponding Weir Hazard Level.

A. TOWBACK   **SCORE**

No visible towback	0
< 1m	1
1 - 2m	2
2 - 3m	3
3 - 4m	4
> 4m	5

B. DEPTH OF HYDRAULIC/STOPPER

No visible hydraulic/stopper	0
< 0.3m	1
0.3 - 1m	2
> 1m	3

C. HEIGHT OF DROP OVER WEIR

No visible drop	0
< 0.3m	1
0.3 - 1m	2
1 - 2.5m	3
> 2.5m	4

D. SLOPE OF WEIR FACE (see fig 1)

Structure drowned out - no weir face present	0
> 60°	1
45° - 60°	2
30° - 45°	3
< 30°	4

E. FLOATING DEBRIS IN HYDRAULIC/STOPPER

No floating debris	0
Up to 10% of hole contains debris	2
10 - 25% of hole contains debris	3
> 25% of hole contains debris	4

F. UNIFORMITY OF HYDRAULIC/STOPPER

No visible hydraulic/stopper	0
Broken feature with multiple flush points or 1 main flush point	1
One or two small flush points in the hydraulic/stopper	2
Totally uniform with no breaks and flush points	5

G. SIDES OF HYDRAULIC/STOPPER

Both open	0
One side open/one side closed	2
Both closed	4

H. ORIENTATION OF HYDRAULIC/STOPPER TO FLOW (see fig 2)

No hydraulic/stopper present	0
< 30° to current	1
> 30 but < 90° to current	2
90° to current	3

I. ADDITIONAL HAZARDS IN OR DOWNSTREAM OF WEIR
  eg strainers, weirs or significant rapids

No additional hazards	0
Hazard present but not in main flow	1
Hazard present in main flow	5

J. COMPOSITION OF RIVER BED AT THE BASE OF WEIR

Structure drowned out/non-modular	0
Concrete	1
Sand or gravel	2
Rock or debris	3

WEIR HAZARD SCORE:
Sum of scores selected for each hazard

WEIR HAZARD LEVEL:
Corresponding Hazard Level from table below   ( )

Weir Hazard Level:

Hazard Score	>0-10	11-15	16-20	21-30	31-40
Hazard Level	V Low (1)	Low (2)	Med (3)	High (4)	V High (5)

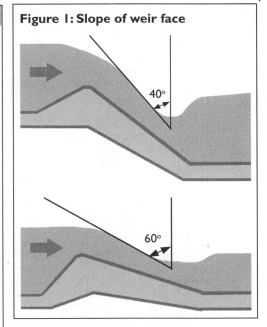

Figure 1: Slope of weir face

40°

60°

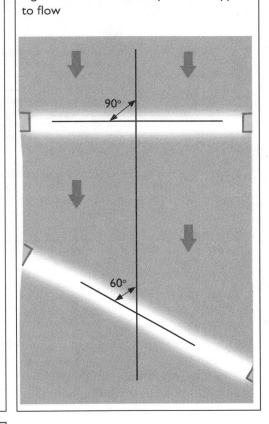

Figure 2: Orientation of hydraulic/stopper to flow

90°

60°

8

3

2. LIKELIHOOD OF WEIR TO CAUSE HARM

How to use this table:
For each consideration, select one description and circle the corresponding score. Add up the circled scores and write the total in the Likelihood of Weir to Cause Harm box.

SCORE

PUBLIC ACCESS

Public access from land and water – is the structure in a publicly accessed location?

Land upstream river right	no public access from land/bank	0
	public access from land/bank	0.25
Land upstream river left	no public access from land/bank	0
	public access from land/bank	0.25
Land downstream river right	no public access from land/bank	0
	public access from land/bank	0.25
Land downstream river left	no public access from land/bank	0
	public access from land/bank	0.25
Water upstream	no access to weir from upstream	0
	access to weir from upstream	0.5
Water downstream	no access to weir from downstream	0
	access to weir from downstream	0.5

CONTROL MEASURES

Are there control measures in place, eg fences or booms, to prevent people from entering the weir?

Land:

Upstream river left	adequate control measures in place	0
	inadequate control measures in place	0.25
Upstream river right	adequate control measures in place	0
	inadequate control measures in place	0.25
Downstream river left	adequate control measures in place	0
	inadequate control measures in place	0.25
Downstream river right	adequate control measures in place	0
	inadequate control measures in place	0.25

Water:

Upstream	Structure not in main channel/boom present	0
	Structure in main channel/no boom present	0.5
Downstream	Controlled by boom or by high speed of water	0
	No downstream control measures	0.5

ABILITY TO SELF-RESCUE

Taking into account the existing control measures, if a person were to fall into the water above/beyond/outside the existing control measures can they self rescue before entering the weir?

Upstream river left	can self-rescue	0
	can't self rescue	0.25
Upstream river right	can self-rescue	0
	can't self rescue	0.25
Downstream river left	can self-rescue	0
	can't self rescue	0.25
Downstream river right	can self-rescue	0
	can't self rescue	0.25

SECTIONS OF A RIVER

The river/waterway can be divided into four sections for ease of identification: upstream and downstream of the weir/hazard and river left and river right. This is always done from the perspective of looking downstream.

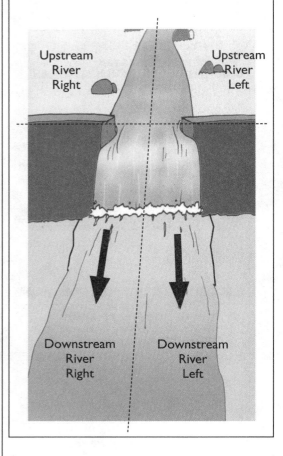

LIKELIHOOD OF WEIR TO CAUSE HARM	
Sum of scores selected for each consideration	

LIKELIHOOD OF WEIR TO CAUSE HARM LEVEL:	( )
Corresponding Likelihood Level from table below	

Likelihood Level:

Likelihood Score	0-1	>1-2	>2-3	>3-4	>4-5
Likelihood Level	V Unlikely (1)	Unlikely (2)	Likely (3)	V Likely (4)	Almost certain (5)

4　© Natural Resources Wales / Rescue 3 Europe Mar 2016 v3.2

8

3. WEIR RISK RATING

Risk = Hazard x Likelihood

The Hazard and the Likelihood have been calculated in the previous tables.

Using these results, the Weir Risk Rating Score can be calculated:

WEIR HAZARD LEVEL:
Level of 1-5 taken from Table 1 (page 3)

LIKELIHOOD OF WEIR TO CAUSE HARM LEVEL:
Level of 1-5 taken from Table 2 (opposite)

WEIR RISK RATING SCORE:
Multiply Hazard Level by Likelihood Level (from above)

WEIR RISK RATING LEVEL:
Corresponding description from table below i.e. Low

Likelihood \ Hazard	1 Very Low	2 Low	3 Medium	4 High	5 Very High
1 Very Unlikely	1	2	3	4	5
2 Unlikely	2	4	6	8	10
3 Likely	3	6	9	12	15
4 Very Likely	4	8	12	16	20
5 Almost Certain	5	10	15	20	25

Score	Risk Level	Action
1 - 5	LOW	Action required to reduce the risk, although low priority. Time, effort and cost should be proportional to the risk.
6 - 10	MEDIUM	Action required soon to control. Interim measures may be necessary in the short term.
12 - 25	HIGH	Action required urgently to control the risks. Further resources may be needed.

5

4. WEIR RESCUE

How to use this table:
For each rescue consideration, select one description and circle the corresponding score.
Add up the circled scores and write the total in the Weir Rescue Difficulty box.

	SCORE
A. DISTANCE ACROSS WEIR/RIVER	
< 10m	1
10 - 20m	2
21 - 50m	3
51 - 75m	4
> 75m	5
B. ACCESS TO BOTH BANKS	
Easy access to both banks for people & vehicles	0
Easy access to both banks for people only	1
Easy access to only 1 bank for vehicles & people	2
Easy access to only one bank for people	3
Difficult / restricted access to both banks for people & vehicles	4
No access to either bank	5
C. SHAPE OF WEIR	
Straight	1
Curved/multi-directional/compound structure	3
D. TOWBACK	
No visible towback	0
< 1m	1
1 - 2m	2
2 - 3m	3
3 - 4m	4
> 4m	5
E. REMOTENESS	
Urban	1
Rural/semi-urban	2
Remote	4
F. NATURE OF RIVER DOWNSTREAM OF WEIR (see opposite)	
Up to Class I	1
Class II	2
Class III	3
> Class III	4
Additional downstream weirs	5
G. WORKING AREA ON BANKS	
Good working areas on both banks	1
Good working areas on one bank only	2
Limited or restricted working areas on both banks	3
No working areas on either bank	4
H. ANCHORS FOR ROPE SYSTEM	
Good anchor points on both banks	1
Good anchor points on one bank only	2
Limited anchor points on both banks	3
I. AVAILABLE RESCUE TECHNIQUES	
Full range of single and twin bank methods with easy ability to cross channel with ropes, eg bridge, short throw or shallow crossing	0
Full range of single and twin bank methods but difficult to cross channel with ropes, eg bridge, short throw or shallow crossing	1
Limited to single bank methods or use of paddle boat	2
Limited to single bank methods or use of motorised boat	3
No bank-based options available	4
Helicopter only	5
Helicopter not possible (overhead wires etc)	6
J. HEIGHT OF BANKS ABOVE BASE OF HYDRAULIC/STOPPER	
< 1m	1
1 - 3m	2
> 3m	3

8

WEIR RESCUE DIFFICULTY SCORE: [ ]
Sum of scores selected for each rescue

WEIR RESCUE DIFFICULTY LEVEL: [ ] ( )
Corresponding Difficulty Level from table below

Weir Rescue Difficulty Level:

Difficulty Score	< 20	20-25	> 25
Difficulty Level	Low (1)	Medium (2)	High (3)

6   © Natural Resources Wales / Rescue 3 Europe Mar 2016 v3.2

International River Grading System

Class I
Clear section of moving water or simple rapid which may contain low waves and few or no obstructions. Clear route through section of river.

Class II
Medium rapid which may contain irregular waves, small stoppers and simple obstructions. Clear route through section of river.

Class III
Larger rapid which may contain medium, irregular waves, medium stoppers and multiple obstructions. Recognisable route between obstructions/features.

> Class III
Heavy rapid which may contain high, irregular waves, large stoppers and numerous obstructions. No easily recognisable route between obstructions/features.

NOTES

Mud, ice and unstable surface considerations

Although not generally a water or flood hazard, it is not uncommon for teams of rescue technicians to be asked to help at or undertake rescue from mud and ice – often collectively treated as unstable surfaces.

Although not exactly a water rescue, there are many similarities. Many of the skills, equipment and PPE used at a mud or ice rescue are the same as for water and flooding incidents.

Ideally a pre-plan should exist for areas which are prone to incidents involving mud. There will be a provision of specialist equipment, such as water or air injection lances, and inflatable rescue platforms or sleds.

Clearly if a victim (human or animal) has fallen through ice or sunk in mud, then a rescuer will suffer the same fate if they should venture out unaided. Therefore, a method of spreading weight and aiding maneuverability, such as an inflatable rescue platform, sled or board is required.

By using an aid, the rescuer will be able to cross the unstable ground to reach the victim.

Ice

People tend to only get into problems when the ice is no longer able to support them and they now end up in the water.

If a victim is under the ice, then specialist dive rescue teams are required. As long as the victim remains at the surface, then more general water rescue techniques may be successfully applied. If the rescuers have to access the victim over the ice, then full PPE for water should be worn.

Techniques need to be used to ensure that the rescuers do not fall through the ice. This means spreading their weight out over a larger area with objects that will float should the ice fail. Commonly, this is achieved through the use of inflatable pathways or rescue sleds. Two inflatable pathways can be leapfrogged out to the victim.

A more detailed look at ice rescue is available in Rescue 3's Surface Ice Rescue Technician course.

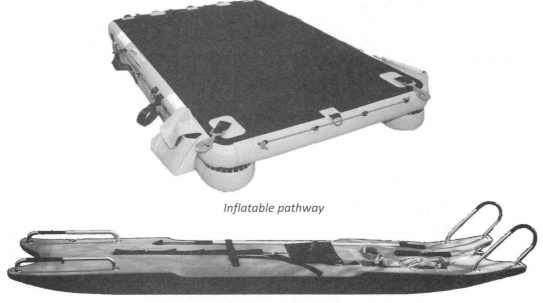

Inflatable pathway

Mayday Hansa Board

Mud

Two of the main approaches to mud rescue are the same as for ice rescue, namely the use of paired inflatable pathways or mud sleds. Alternatively, for large areas of mud, hovercrafts have proven very successful.

Depending upon the constituents of the mud, it will have very different properties and thus respond to different rescue approaches. The common techniques for releasing people or animals trapped in mud are:

Air injection

This is achieved through the use of a specialist mud lance connected to a breathing apparatus cylinder. This allows for compressed air to be forced into the mud, which will hopefully help release a trapped person. In certain mud types, this can be very successful.

Water injection

An alternative approach is force water into the mud. Again, depending upon mud type, this can also be successful. This can potentially be achieved through use of a fire hose and appliance. Alternatively, fire extinguishers have been successfully used and can operate remotely.

Digging

This is probably the highest risk approach for the victim of a mud entrapment. As victims struggle in an attempt to avoid entrapment, their limbs can end up being spread out and in odd positions. Additionally, the effects of compression from the mud and cold can result in the victim losing feeling in their limbs. As a result, it is difficult for rescuers to dig around the victim and know they are not going to hit a limb. Should they do so, it may not initially be felt by the victim and severe damage may be the result of continued impact.

Hazardous material and decontamination issues

Mud rescues generate significant hazmat and decontamination issues. The mud may well contain significant physical, chemical and biological hazards in addition to the entrapment hazard. Effective PPE will be needed for rescuers. Although this will be very similar to their existing water PPE, it will ideally be a separate set of equipment dedicated for mud rescue, due to the difficulty of cleaning residual mud from the clothing.

8

Rescues from vehicles in water

A more detailed look at the issues associated with rescues from vehicles in water is available through the Rescue 3 Rescues from Vehicles in Water (RVW) course.

Rescues from vehicles are one of the most common water-related incidents faced by the rescue services.

Sixty percent of flood deaths in the USA are attributed to people driving their vehicles into moving water. In the UK summer floods of 2007, over 70% of the rescues carried out in the Hereford floods involved vehicles in water. The pressures on the rescuers to act are often great. Changeable conditions and problems such as access, stability, extrication, communication, crew safety, time constraints and entrapment all have to be overcome.

The stages of a rescue involving a vehicle in water are the same as any other water rescue.

- Locate
- Access
- Stabilize
- Transport

The common problems are:

Access

It is common to have to access the vehicle or its immediate area and a decision about stabilizing the vehicle will need to be made. Rescues must assess whether or not at any moment the vehicle could move. Rescuers are at greater risk during this period. In order to access suitable anchor points on the vehicle, windows may need to be opened, removed or broken. This involves specialist glass management training and skills.

This could also destabilize the situation by changing the hydrology surrounding the car, and also has the potential of flushing victims.

Stabilization

This is a key requirement in order to secure operational time, ensure the safety of rescuers, and increase the potential success of any rescue. Verbal or hand signal contact should be made with any victims and to help keep them from acting in a way that could make their situation worse.

Extrication

It may be necessary to extricate passengers from the vehicle. This involves similar skill sets as dealing with road traffic collisions, but in a very different environment.

Hazardous materials

For vehicle rescue tasks, extra PPE should be considered to mitigate against the extra hazards posed by the vehicle, e.g., safety glasses and gloves that are designed to protect the hands from sharp edges.

Consideration should be given to the presence of hazardous materials, such as gas, diesel and battery acid, which may have leaked into the water. As well as the environmental effects, these may also attack ropes, technical equipment, PPE and deteriorate seals on dry suits, as well as be skin irritants. All equipment should be decontaminated and checked after use.

Vehicle-specific hazards

The electrical system of a vehicle is an unknown entity when immersed. Generally, it will cease functioning soon after immersion and render all the lights, safety systems and other electrical functions inoperable. However, there are cases reported where the lights, wipers, radios and horns of an immersed vehicle operate sporadically for a considerable time.

It is usual operational procedure to disable electrical systems prior to extrication, to reduce fire risk and to disarm safety systems such as airbags. Due to the nature of water incidents, it is not usually possible to disconnect the power. With this in mind, rescuers should treat all safety systems as active, and due care should be taken not to encroach into the deployment zones of airbags.

Rescuers need knowledge of the water and associated features to enable them to assess the scene, and develop an action plan. By having a practical understanding of hydrology, they can understand the forces at work upon the vehicle, where to best gain access to the vehicle, where to extricate its occupants from, and where to evacuate them to.

Vehicle anatomy

It is essential that rescuers have a basic understanding of the features and terminology associated with vehicles. With this knowledge they can use common terms along with other rescue services.

The posts supporting the vehicle roof are named alphabetically from front (the A posts) to back. These posts are designed to be strong points and support the integrity of the passenger cell. The front and rear cantrails run between the two A posts and rear posts. They also support the roof panel.

Body panels are designed to add strength to the vehicle. This is done by shaping panels in such a way to help prevent them buckling under pressure.

8

Glass management

Rescuers should try to leave as many windows in place as possible. It is likely that in order to secure the vehicle, windows will have to be broken to allow an anchor point to be made. This must be assessed carefully. Additionally, glass may have to be removed to extricate the victims. Where possible, the victims should assist by opening the window themselves from the inside.

There are several different types of glass found in vehicles:

Toughened glass

Toughened glass is usually fitted to the side and rear windows. Toughened glass will shatter into small cubes when hit with a hammer or a window punch. The broken glass can then be easily cleared away.

Laminated glass

Laminated glass has a thin layer of plastic sandwiched between two layers of glass. Laminated glass is designed not to shatter, but to either chip or crack. If the windscreen is hit by a stone chip when driving, the driver can carry on in relative safety. On high-end cars, laminated glass is sometimes fitted to the rear and side windows for increased security.

Dealing with laminated glass can be time-consuming and awkward. This is why many teams leave them in place. It is easier to remove the toughened glass side windows. When dealing with road traffic collisions (RTCs), to prevent uncontrolled breakages, the glass will either be removed in one piece, broken under control, or left intact.

Removing windows from a vehicle will alter its balance and integrity. Rescuers should consider the possibility of the car flooding and altering its stability. Normally, the preferred windows to remove are on the downstream side of the vehicle, where the pressure is less and the chance of the vehicle flooding is less.

Vehicle hydrology

A vehicle in moving water will create much the same water features as an obstacle such as a rock. All the same principles apply.

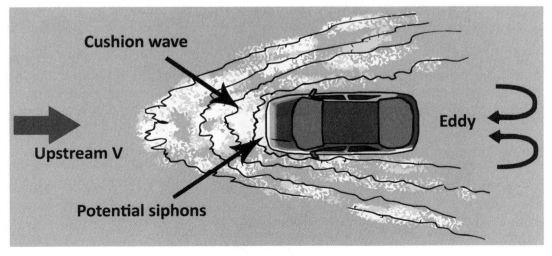

Vehicle hydrology

The high pressure area on the upstream side of the vehicle will make it a difficult area in which to work. If there is a space between the vehicle and the ground, then this space will allow moving water to flow through it, creating a siphon effect. Clearly, if water is flowing through this gap, then it is likely that debris and possibly a person could get pushed into it and become pinned. This is precisely why the high pressure, upstream side of the vehicle should be avoided.

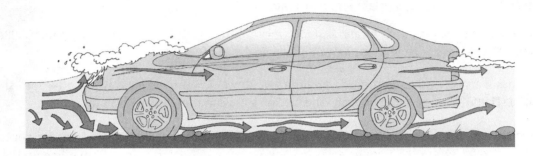

The siphon hazard of a car is clearly shown from the side.

The low pressure, downstream side will be much easier for the rescuers. However, should the vehicle dislodge, it will move downstream into this low pressure area onto the rescuers. Before any rescuer is committed into this area, it is essential the vehicle is stable.

Vehicle behavior in water

The behavior of a vehicle in water is not an exact science. However, by studying past incidents, and looking at research done in the USA, we can start to predict a trend as to how a vehicle could be expected to behave.

As a general rule, a vehicle which has moved with the water will come to rest with the engine pointing upstream. This is because the engine compartment is the heaviest part of the vehicle.

The stability of the vehicle in moving water is largely dependent on the type of ground underneath it.

On soft ground, the wheels are likely to sink in. The water pressure will push down on the body and anchor the car down. As a result, the siphon effect may be reduced, but the cushion wave will increase. When bedded into soft ground, the vehicle is less likely to roll but still may require anchoring.

When on hard ground, such as the road, the wheels cannot bed down. Depending on the volume and force of water flowing, the vehicle is more likely to slide or roll downstream. In this situation securing the car quickly is paramount.

Wherever possible, the occupants should be encouraged to remain still, to prevent altering the stability of the vehicle once it has come to rest. A stable vehicle is much easier to deal with than a moving one. Imagine dealing with an RTC on the motorway with the vehicle slowly moving along the road.

If a vehicle moves or rolls, it is likely to sustain further damage which will create problems of water ingress, gaining access to damaged doors and panels, as well as injuries to occupants.

While previous events suggest a trend for how a vehicle reacts in the water, it is only to be used as a guide. There are many unseen forces at work, and the unpredictable can happen at any time. If possible, the vehicle is stabilized as early as possible and the risks assessed continually.

8

Accessing a vehicle

Once a plan has been formed, the rescuers will need to gain access to the vehicle in the water. Access techniques are detailed earlier in this manual. The priority at the vehicle is to establish secure anchors. Rescuers should avoid entering the vehicle until it has been securely anchored or deemed stable.

It is likely that rescuers will only have access from one bank initially. The decision will have to be made whether to use both banks or to remain operating from one side.

The presence of snag hazards, such as aerials, door mirrors, wipers, and damaged body panels, all add to the difficulty and risk when working with ropes around a vehicle in the water.

Anchor points

During the initial assessment, rescuers should decide how to secure the vehicle to limit any further movement. Strong points on vehicles are the upright posts, wheels, axles, and towing points. Depending on the situation, it will usually be difficult to secure anywhere apart from the upright posts, as all of the other points will be underwater.

To secure to the posts, either glass must be removed, the windows opened, or the door opened. Where possible, steel strops or protected webbing loops should be used, as there may be sharp edges, hot metal, and contaminants present.

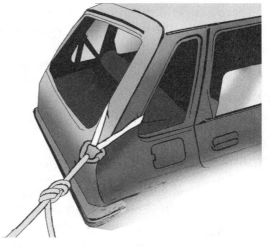

Different anchor points

Vehicle stabilization

How a vehicle can best be stabilized can only be decided at the time of an incident, taking into account a number of factors. These include:

- Assess the size of the vehicle, type of bottom, flow levels, etc. And determine how likely the vehicle is to move
- Is there access to both banks?
- Can the vehicle be secured to both banks?
- Where are suitable anchors points located on the banks?
- If the vehicle can only be secured to one bank, what direction could it move in?

In order to answer these and other questions arising, rescuers need to be able to read the water conditions. Rescuers will need the necessary rope skills to create safe and effective anchor and belay systems.

Remember that the potential loads created by vehicles in flowing water could be very large. They are a result of the following:

- Vehicle size, shape and mass
- Water velocity
- Water depth
- Nature of the ground the vehicle is on
- Whether the vehicle is pinned against another object
- Number of people in/on the vehicle

Some of these factors are relative constants (e.g., vehicle size), while others are variable. The loads on any stabilization ropes will be affected by changes in water levels or, in the case of small vehicles, changing the number of people on the vehicle.

With the potential for large loads, careful considerations must be given to the methods of anchoring and the equipment that is used.

Anchor systems

- Backing-up of anchor points
- Combining several anchors into one bombproof anchor
- Using load-sharing anchors if the vehicle can be stabilized from both banks
- Using load-distributing anchors if potential movement of an anchored vehicle still exists.
- Use of multiple ropes and independent anchors to create redundancy
- Use of appropriate mechanical advantage and belay systems

Belay systems

- Is a controlled release possible?

Equipment

- Choice of rope type (some vehicles weigh more than the rope is rated for)
- Protecting rope and equipment from edges and glass hazards
- Use of improvised dampening systems to protect personnel should equipment failure occur
- Logging of all equipment use and retirement following exposure to excessive loads or adverse conditions, e.g., chemical contamination

Extrication of victims

The rescuers must decide, during their scene size-up, which is the best way to extricate the occupants of the vehicle. Depending on the orientation of the car in the flow of water, it may be that the downstream doors or a window are the only options. However, the sunroof (if fitted) could also be considered.

Care must taken to check the number of occupants in the vehicle. Not all may be visible, for instance a child secured in a safety seat will be below the window line and possibly below the water level.

Rescuers should use PFDs for the victims. A PFD will assist the rescuers with handling the victim and provide additional buoyancy.

Where possible, the victims must be encouraged to remain still inside the vehicle. Often when rescuers approach, the victims will move towards them in the belief they are helping. In fact, they may seriously affect the stabilization of the vehicle, making the incident worse.

It is likely that to secure the vehicle at least two windows will have to be opened or broken to allow the anchor webbing to be fixed. These windows could also be then used to extricate the victims. If the vehicle is sideways to the flow, then it may be possible to open the downstream doors to extricate the victims. Care must be taken not to make openings on the upstream side which will alter the stability, and possibly wash the victims out of the vehicle. Commonly, vehicles come to rest with the engine upstream. By using a shallow water wedge, rescuers can create an eddy which can allow the side doors to be opened.

When deciding on openings, rescuers should attempt to choose the largest available, such as the rear window or tailgate, as this will ease the extrication of victims. Hopefully, the extrication can take place without the need to use hydraulic tools to cut away or ram body panels to create space, as this will make the job much more complex. It is often best to avoid the laminated front windscreen, due to difficulty in removal. It is also likely that the front is facing upstream, so the integrity of the windscreen is useful to prevent water ingress and to add strength to the front of the vehicle.

Victim handling could be difficult under the circumstances. If the victims are to be moved to a boat, it should be positioned as close as possible, which will help with the handling issues. Rescuers will have to be positive and take control of the situation, often taking a firm grip of victims as they are assisted from the vehicle. If the victim is unable to assist with their own extrication due to injury, then the rescuers may have to use extra equipment dependent on injury, such as backboards (as with a road-based RTC).

Additional problems

Rescuers should consider the use of a hydraulic platform to have a bank-based extended reach capability. Consider mobilizing a tow truck to assist with stabilization or the possible removal of the vehicle from the water.

It is not an acceptable risk for rescuers to attempt improvised sub-surface rescues in any form. Even to duck under the water momentarily carries enormous risk. The danger of entrapment is massive.

There is no hard and fast rule which states a passenger compartment will maintain an air pocket for a given amount of time. History dictates all scenarios are different - sometimes a vehicle floods immediately and sometimes it takes a while. No rules exist, other than it is highly dangerous to risk going under the water and into a vehicle without the correct training and equipment.

8

Helicopter familiarization

There is no doubt that helicopters can be a vital asset in water and flood rescue. The 2005 flooding by Hurricane Katrina in New Orleans demonstrates how effective, well-coordinated use of rescue helicopters can save lives.

Helicopters have the capability to reduce time taken, both in the deployment of rescuers and the transportation of victims. Those helicopters equipped with winches have the potential to undertake mid-channel and over-water pickups. They can greatly increase search capability through increased visibility and use of specialist tools such as forward-looking infrared (FLIR) cameras.

Helicopters can also create problems at water and flood incidents, such as noise and downwash from the rotors. There can be communication difficulties between rescue teams on the ground and rescue helicopters overhead, due to different radio equipment.

Sometimes, a helicopter is the only option. At other times, while the use of a helicopter might be of benefit, rescuers should not be helicopter-reliant. If possible, rescuers should begin to undertake alternative rescue methods, rather than waiting for a helicopter to arrive.

Rescuers should differentiate between helicopter-supported rescue and helicopter-based rescues.

Helicopter-supported rescues

Here the helicopter may transport personnel and equipment to the rescue site where a landing zone is established. Once the rescue is completed, the helicopter may be used for transporting patients to further medical assistance.

Helicopter-based rescues

Here the helicopter deploys rescuers or evacuates victims directly from the rescue site. This includes techniques such as hoist operations, short hauls, single skid landings, etc.

8

Helicopter rules:

1. Do not approach without receiving a visual signal from the pilot. Never leave without a visual or spoken instruction to do so. Stay where the pilot can see you at all times.

2. On sloping ground always approach or leave on the downslope side for maximum rotor clearance.

3. If blinded by swirling dust or grit, STOP - crouch lower or sit down and wait for assistance.

4. Never approach or leave a helicopter when its engine and rotors are running down or starting up.

5. Crouch while walking for extra rotor clearance. Always remove hats. Never reach up or chase after anything that blows away.

6. Carry long objects horizontally below waist level - never upright or on the shoulder.

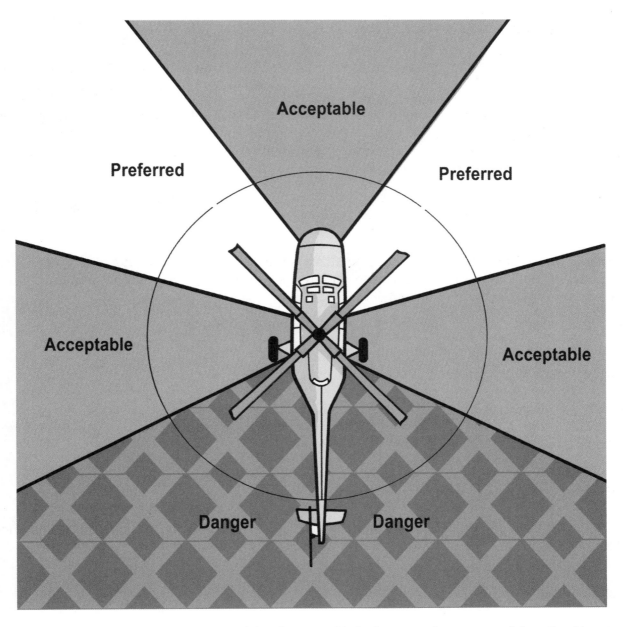

For helicopters like the S76 or UH-60 with low front rotor blade clearance, always approach from the side.

APPENDICES

SECTION CONTENTS

Personal equipment list

All Swiftwater and Flood Rescue Technicians need to be suitably equipped to be able to carry out the their role.

This equipment must be in good order, tested, maintained and should conform to the relevant USGC and UL standards where they exist.

Basic equipment requirements are discussed on page 52.

In addition to that equipment, it is advisable that a technician also carries:

- Waterproof headlamp which can be helmet-mounted
- Three locking carabiners (HMS shape preferred)
- 9ft (3m) length of webbing
- Cowstail with locking carabiner (for use with a quick-release chest harness)
- A Prusik-minding pulley
- Two Prusik loops
- Waterproof notepad and pencil
- Window (center) punch

Although this appears to be relatively little, if every technician carries those few extra items, when that equipment is pooled, there is a useful quantity of equipment.

Team equipment list

The amount of team equipment will vary depending upon team background, role and area of operation. A list for team equipment should be similar to the list below. This gives the technicians enough equipment to undertake the rescue techniques they have been trained for.

An initial response team will tend to travel light, whereas a full emergency service team will have the capacity to carry a larger range of gear.

Recommended SRT team equipment list

(Based on a minimum of 4 team members)

- 4 x floating ropes (minimum length of 150'-300')
- 1 x low stretch kernmantle ropes (minimum length of 150'-300')
- 25 x locking carabiners
- 3 x pulleys (Prusik-minding if using Prusiks)
- 3 x rope grabs or Prusik loops
- 2 x belay devices
- Lengths of webbing and/or selection of sewn slings
- 2 x rope protectors
- Bags for ropes and technical hardware
- Boat for tethering, paddling and wading (must be suitable design for operational area)
- 6 x paddles
- 2 pairs of fins
- Poles (non-metal) for shallow water techniques
- Litter basket
- Spinal backboard
- Victim PFDs (adult and child)
- Medical kit
- Decontamination equipment
- Scene lighting
- Search lighting
- Handheld waterproof radio communications
- Basic life support equipment
- Oxygen administration equipment

Fire service teams will generally also have access to:

- Hose inflation equipment
- 2 x inflatable rescue platforms
- Compressed air cylinders

Notes

Notes

Notes